Algebra
Workbook II

Table of Contents

Solving Equations Review

Level ☆

Score

/100

Date / / Name

1 Solve each equation.

5 points per question

Examples

$$x - 4 = 5$$
$$x = 5 + 4$$
$$x = 9$$

$$3 + x = 10$$
$$x = 10 - 3$$
$$x = 7$$

To solve equations, think in terms of "$x = $ a number." For questions such as the examples above, add or subtract a number on both sides of the equal sign.

(1) $x - 3 = 8$

(6) $x + 1 = \dfrac{1}{4}$

(2) $1 + x = 7$

(7) $x - \dfrac{1}{3} = 2$

(3) $x - 5 = -4$

(8) $\dfrac{1}{4} + x = \dfrac{1}{3}$

(4) $3 + x = -5$

(9) $\dfrac{2}{3} + x = -3$

(5) $-2 + x = -6$

(10) $-\dfrac{5}{2} + x = -\dfrac{2}{3}$

To check if your answer is correct, substitute your value for x into the original equation.

2 **Solve each equation.**

Examples

$$3x = 12$$
$$x = 12 \times \frac{1}{3}$$
$$x = 4$$

$$-\frac{1}{4}x = 7$$
$$x = 7 \times (-4)$$
$$x = -28$$

For questions such as the examples above, multiply both sides of the equal sign by a number.

(1) $2x = 10$

(2) $\frac{1}{3}x = -8$

(3) $-9x = 12$

(4) $6x = -6$

(5) $-\frac{1}{5}x = -2$

(6) $\frac{2}{3}x = 5$

(7) $-\frac{4}{3}x = 6$

(8) $5x = -\frac{1}{3}$

(9) $-\frac{3}{4}x = -\frac{1}{2}$

(10) $-\frac{5}{2}x = -\frac{5}{4}$

You're off to a great start!

2 Solving Equations Review

Date   /   /

Name

Score   /100

1 Solve each equation.

6 points per question

Example

$$6x - 11 = 4x - 3$$
$$6x - 4x = -3 + 11$$
$$2x = 8$$
$$x = 4$$

Transposition (or **Inverse Operations**) is when we move a term to the other side of the equation and change the sign.

(1) $7x + 8 = 5x + 14$

(2) $8x + 4 = 5x + 10$

(3) $10x + 1 = 9x - 3$

(4) $3x - 3 = 5x + 7$

(5) $2x - 1 = -2x + 5$

(6) $-6x - 2 = -x + 12$

(7) $\dfrac{1}{2}x + 6 = -\dfrac{3}{2}x - 1$

(8) $-\dfrac{1}{3}x + \dfrac{1}{2} = -\dfrac{2}{5}x + \dfrac{1}{4}$

2 Solve each equation, and check your answer.

Example

$$7x - 6 = 4x + 9$$
$$7x - 4x = 9 + 6$$
$$3x = 15$$
$$x = 5$$

Check !

Left side $= 7 \times 5 - 6 = 35 - 6 = 29$

Right side $= 4 \times 5 + 9 = 20 + 9 = 29$

If the value on the left side of the equal sign matches the value on the right, then your answer is correct.

(1) $3x - 6 = x + 8$

Check!

Left side =

Right side =

(2) $2x + 15 = 9x - 6$

Check!

Left side =

Right side =

(3) $-\dfrac{1}{3}x + \dfrac{1}{2} = \dfrac{5}{3}x - \dfrac{3}{2}$

Check!

Left side =

Right side =

(4) $-\dfrac{1}{2}x - \dfrac{1}{3} = -\dfrac{3}{4}x + \dfrac{2}{3}$

Check!

Left side =

Right side =

Get in the habit of double checking your answers!

Date / /

Name

Score

/100

1 Solve each equation.

6 points per question

Examples

$$2(3x+4)=-4$$
$$6x+8=-4$$
$$6x=-12$$
$$x=-2$$

$$\frac{1}{2}x+\frac{1}{6}=\frac{1}{3}$$
$$\left(\frac{1}{2}x+\frac{1}{6}\right)\times 6=\left(\frac{1}{3}\right)\times 6$$
$$3x+1=2$$
$$3x=1$$
$$x=\frac{1}{3}$$

To simplify an equation, remove the parentheses and denominators.

(1) $3(x+2)=-9$

(4) $\frac{1}{4}x+\frac{1}{3}=\frac{1}{6}$

To remove denominators, multiply each side by the least common multiple (LCM) of the denominators.

(2) $3(3x-2)=2(2x+2)$

(5) $\frac{2}{3}x-1=-\frac{1}{8}+\frac{3}{4}x$

(3) $-(x-1)=-4(2-x)$

2 **Solve each equation for** x.

Examples

$$x+2=a \qquad\qquad a=b-x \qquad\qquad 2x=a-b$$

$$x=a-2 \qquad\qquad x=-a+b \qquad\qquad x=\frac{a-b}{2}$$

Transpose as necessary to formulate each question as "$x=$ a number."

(1) $x+3=y$

(2) $c=-b-x$

(3) $x-y=-w$

(4) $-3=-f-x$

(5) $w=-8-x$

(6) $4x=-b$

(7) $-ax=-b$

(8) $9x=4a+b$

(9) $ax=-2b+3c$

(10) $rx-s=4t$

You're acing this review section!

Simultaneous Linear Equations Review

Date   /   /

Name

1   **Solve each equation for both variables by using the subtraction method.**

10 points per question

Example

$$\begin{cases} 4x + 5y = 7 & \cdots ① \\ x + 5y = 13 & \cdots ② \end{cases}$$

Subtraction method

Step 1: Number each equation.

$$
\begin{array}{rl}
① - ②: & 4x + 5y = 7 \quad \cdots ① \\
-) & x + 5y = 13 \quad \cdots ② \\
\hline
& 3x \quad\quad = -6 \\
& x \quad\quad = -2
\end{array}
$$

Step 2: Remove a variable by subtracting one equation from the other.

Substitute this into ②:

$$
\begin{aligned}
-2 + 5y &= 13 \\
5y &= 15 \\
y &= 3
\end{aligned}
$$

Step 3: Substitute the value of the variable into either original equation (usually the simpler one) to solve for the other variable.

⟨**Ans.**⟩ $(x, y) = (-2, 3)$

Step 4: Write your answer.

(1) $\begin{cases} 7x + 4y = 1 \\ 5x + 4y = 3 \end{cases}$

(3) $\begin{cases} -4x + 3y = -14 \\ -4x - 2y = 6 \end{cases}$

⟨**Ans.**⟩ _____

⟨**Ans.**⟩ _____

(2) $\begin{cases} 2x - 6y = 10 \\ 2x + y = -11 \end{cases}$

(4) $\begin{cases} -3x + 6y = 5 \\ x + 6y = -7 \end{cases}$

⟨**Ans.**⟩ _____

⟨**Ans.**⟩ _____

2 **Solve each equation for both variables by using the addition method.** 15 points per question

Example

$$\begin{cases} 3x + 2y = 12 & \cdots ① \\ 5x - 2y = 4 & \cdots ② \end{cases}$$

Addition method

Step 1: Number each equation.

$$① + ② : \quad \begin{array}{r} 3x + 2y = 12 \quad \cdots ① \\ +\ )\ 5x - 2y = 4 \quad \cdots ② \\ \hline 8x \quad\quad = 16 \\ x \quad\quad = 2 \end{array}$$

Step 2: Remove a variable by adding one equation to the other.

Substitute this into ② :
$$\begin{array}{r} 10 - 2y = 4 \\ -2y = -6 \\ y = 3 \end{array}$$

Step 3: Substitute the value of the variable into either original equation (usually the simpler one) to solve for the other variable.

⟨Ans.⟩ $(x, y) = (2, 3)$

Step 4: Write your answer.

(1) $\begin{cases} 4x - 3y = 2 \\ -x + 3y = -5 \end{cases}$

(3) $\begin{cases} x + 3y = 2 \\ \dfrac{1}{4}x - 3y = 3 \end{cases}$

⟨Ans.⟩ _____

⟨Ans.⟩ _____

(2) $\begin{cases} 5x - 2y = -9 \\ -5x - y = 0 \end{cases}$

(4) $\begin{cases} -\dfrac{1}{2}x + 2y = -1 \\ \dfrac{1}{2}x - 5y = 7 \end{cases}$

⟨Ans.⟩ _____

⟨Ans.⟩ _____

You know this well!

Simultaneous Linear Equations Review

Level

Score

/100

Date / /

Name

1 **Solve each equation.**

20 points per question

Example

$$\begin{cases} 3x - 5y = 2 & \cdots ① \\ x + 2y = 8 & \cdots ② \end{cases}$$

② × 3 : $3x + 6y = 24$ ⋯③

① − ③ : $3x - 5y = 2$ ⋯①

     $-)\ 3x + 6y = 24$ ⋯③

          $-11y = -22$

               $y = 2$

Substitute this into ② :

     $x + 4 = 8$

          $x = 4$

⟨Ans.⟩ $(x, y) = (4, 2)$

Step 1: Number each equation.

Step 2: Multiply one equation by a constant and number the new equation. In this example, we multiplied equation ② by 3 and called it equation ③.

Step 3: Remove a variable by using the addition or subtraction method.

Step 4: Substitute the value of the variable into either original equation (usually the simpler one) to solve for the other variable.

Step 5: Write your answer.

(1) $\begin{cases} 6x + 5y = -3 \\ 3x - 2y = 12 \end{cases}$

(2) $\begin{cases} 5x - 2y = 8 \\ 3x + 8y = 14 \end{cases}$

⟨Ans.⟩

⟨Ans.⟩

10   © *Kumon Publishing Co., Ltd.*

2 Solve each equation, and check your answer.

30 points per question

(1)
$$\begin{cases} x - 2y = -8 & \cdots ① \\ 2x + 3y = -2 & \cdots ② \end{cases}$$

Check!

① : $\boxed{} - 2 \times \boxed{} =$

The left side of ① matches the right!

② : $2 \times \boxed{} + 3 \times \boxed{} =$

The left side of ② matches the right!

〈Ans.〉 _____

(2)
$$\begin{cases} -10x - 9y = -1 \\ 4x - 3y = -4 \end{cases}$$

Check!

〈Ans.〉 _____

Check your answer by substituting the values for x and y into both original equations to be sure that both equations are satisfied.

Checking your work takes time, but it's worth it.

© Kumon Publishing Co., Ltd.

11

Date / /

Name

1 **Solve each equation.** 20 points per question

Example

$$\begin{cases} 5x + 2y = 4 & \cdots ① \\ 7x + 3y = 5 & \cdots ② \end{cases}$$

Step 1: Number each equation.

$① \times 3: \qquad 15x + 6y = 12 \cdots ③$

$② \times 2: \qquad 14x + 6y = 10 \cdots ④$

Step 2: Multiply one equation by a constant and number the new equation.

Step 3: Multiply the other equation by a constant and number the new equation.

$$③ - ④: \qquad \begin{array}{r} 15x + 6y = 12 \cdots ③ \\ -)\ 14x + 6y = 10 \cdots ④ \\ \hline x \qquad\quad = 2 \end{array}$$

Step 4: Remove a variable by using the addition or subtraction method.

Substitute this into ① :

$$10 + 2y = 4$$
$$2y = -6$$
$$y = -3$$

Step 5: Substitute the value of the variable into either original equation (usually the simpler one) to solve for the other variable.

⟨**Ans.**⟩ $(x, y) = (2, -3)$

Step 6: Write your answer.

(1) $\begin{cases} 7x - 3y = 20 & \cdots ① \\ 5x + 4y = 2 & \cdots ② \end{cases}$

(2) $\begin{cases} 3x + 8y = 1 & \cdots ① \\ 5x + 6y = 9 & \cdots ② \end{cases}$

$① \times 3:$

$② \times \boxed{}:$

⟨**Ans.**⟩ _____

⟨**Ans.**⟩ _____

2 Solve each equation, and check your answer.

20 points per question

(1) $\begin{cases} 3x - 7y = -2 \\ 5x - 4y = 12 \end{cases}$

Check!

⟨Ans.⟩ _____

(2) $\begin{cases} 3x + 4y = 24 \\ 5x - 6y = 2 \end{cases}$

Check!

⟨Ans.⟩ _____

(3) $\begin{cases} 6x + 5y = 10 \\ 9x + 8y = 13 \end{cases}$

Check!

⟨Ans.⟩ _____

Remember you have to eliminate one variable in order to solve for the other variable.

Bravo!

13

Simultaneous Linear Equations Review

Level

Date   /   /

Name

Score   /100

---

1   **Solve each equation.**

10 points per question

Example

$$\begin{cases} y = 2x - 3 & \cdots ① \\ 7x - 4y = 8 & \cdots ② \end{cases}$$

Substitution method

Step 1: Number each equation.

Substitute ① into ② :

$$7x - 4(2x - 3) = 8$$
$$7x - 8x + 12 = 8$$
$$-x = -4$$
$$x = 4$$

Step 2: Substitute one equation into the other to remove a variable.

Substitute this into ① :

$$y = 8 - 3$$
$$y = 5$$

Step 3: Substitute the value of the variable into either original equation (usually the simpler one) to solve for the other variable.

⟨**Ans.**⟩ $(x, y) = (4 , 5)$

Step 4: Write your answer.

---

(1) $\begin{cases} y = 3x + 1 \\ x - 2y = 8 \end{cases}$

(3) $\begin{cases} x = -5 - 3y \\ -x - y = -1 \end{cases}$

⟨Ans.⟩ _____

⟨Ans.⟩ _____

(2) $\begin{cases} x = y - 5 \\ 2x - 5y = -4 \end{cases}$

(4) $\begin{cases} 4x - 7y = -3 \\ y = 2 - x \end{cases}$

⟨Ans.⟩ _____

⟨Ans.⟩ _____

  © *Kumon Publishing Co., Ltd.*

2 **Solve each equation by using the substitution method.**

15 points per question

(1) $\begin{cases} 2x + y = -2 & \cdots① \\ 3x + 2y = -1 & \cdots② \end{cases}$

Rewrite ① : $y = \boxed{} x - 2 \cdots③$

Substitute ③ into ② :

⟨Ans.⟩ _____

(3) $\begin{cases} 4x + 3y = -1 & \cdots① \\ 6x + 5y = -3 & \cdots② \end{cases}$

Rewrite ① : $y = \dfrac{\boxed{}}{3} \cdots③$

Substitute ③ into ② :

⟨Ans.⟩ _____

(2) $\begin{cases} 2x - 5y = 5 \\ x + 3y = 8 \end{cases}$

⟨Ans.⟩ _____

(4) $\begin{cases} 5x - 8y = 7 \\ -2x + 7y = 1 \end{cases}$

⟨Ans.⟩ _____

Terrific attention to detail!

Simultaneous Linear Equations Review

Date　　/　　/

Name

Score

/100

1 **Use the following methods to solve the equations** $\begin{cases} x + 3y = -8 & \cdots ① \\ 4x - 3y = 13 & \cdots ② \end{cases}$.

10 points per question

（1）　Addition/subtraction method

（2）　Substitution method

〈Ans.〉

〈Ans.〉

2 **Use the following methods to solve the equations** $\begin{cases} 4x - 3y = 7 & \cdots ① \\ 3x + y = -11 & \cdots ② \end{cases}$.

10 points per question

（1）　Addition/subtraction method

（2）　Substitution method

〈Ans.〉

〈Ans.〉

3 Use the following methods to solve the equations $\begin{cases} 2x - 5y = 5 & \cdots ① \\ -3x + 4y = 3 & \cdots ② \end{cases}$. 15 points per question

(1) Addition/subtraction method

(2) Substitution method

⟨Ans.⟩ _____

⟨Ans.⟩ _____

4 Use the following methods to solve the equations $\begin{cases} 5x + 6y = -16 & \cdots ① \\ -7x - 4y = -4 & \cdots ② \end{cases}$. 15 points per question

(1) Addition/subtraction method

(2) Substitution method

⟨Ans.⟩ _____

⟨Ans.⟩ _____

You can do every method!

1 Solve each equation.

25 points per question

(1) $\begin{cases} x + y + z = 6 & \cdots ① \\ x - 2y + 3z = 1 & \cdots ② \\ x + 3y - z = 8 & \cdots ③ \end{cases}$

Eliminate x:

①－② : $\begin{cases} 3y - 2z = \boxed{} & \cdots ④ \\ -2y + \boxed{}z = \boxed{} & \cdots ⑤ \end{cases}$

④＋⑤ : $y = \boxed{}$

Substitute this into ④ :

$3 \times \boxed{} - 2z = \boxed{}$

$-2z = \boxed{}$

$z = \boxed{}$

Substitute $y = \boxed{}$ and $z = \boxed{}$ into ① :

$x + \boxed{} + \boxed{} = 6$

$x = \boxed{}$

⟨**Ans.**⟩ $(x, y, z) = (\boxed{}, \boxed{}, \boxed{})$

> **Don't forget!**
>
> Three linear equations with the same variables are called **Simultaneous Linear Equations in Three Variables**.
>
> To solve, eliminate one variable so there are only two linear equations with two variables. Then you can use the addition, subtraction, or substitution method to solve.

(2) $\begin{cases} -x + 2y + z = 1 & \cdots ① \\ 2x - 5y - z = 2 & \cdots ② \\ 3x - 7y - z = 3 & \cdots ③ \end{cases}$

Eliminate z:

①＋② :

②－③ :

> Think, "What is the easiest variable to eliminate?"

⟨**Ans.**⟩

2 **Solve each equation.**

25 points per question

(1) $\begin{cases} x - 2y - 4z = 4 & \cdots ① \\ -2x - 2y - 3z = -7 & \cdots ② \\ 3x + 2y - 6z = 2 & \cdots ③ \end{cases}$

Eliminate y :

$① - ②$: $\begin{cases} 3x - z = \boxed{} & \cdots ④ \\ x - \boxed{}z = \boxed{} & \cdots ⑤ \end{cases}$

$⑤ \times 3$:

⟨**Ans.**⟩ _____

(2) $\begin{cases} 3x + y + 2z = 1 & \cdots ① \\ -5x - 3y - 2z = 5 & \cdots ② \\ -9x - 6y - 2z = 13 & \cdots ③ \end{cases}$

⟨**Ans.**⟩ _____

Wow! You can solve for three variables!

19

10

Date   /   /

Name

1 **Solve each equation.**

25 points per question

(1)
$$\begin{cases} 2x - 3y - 4z = -5 & \cdots① \\ x - 5y + 3z = 4 & \cdots② \\ -x + 2y + 3z = 5 & \cdots③ \end{cases}$$

Eliminate x:

② × 2 : $2x - 10y + 6z = 8$ ···④

① − ④ :

② + ③ :

⟨Ans.⟩

(2)
$$\begin{cases} 2x + 3y + 2z = -5 & \cdots① \\ 5x + 6y + 6z = -7 & \cdots② \\ 6x - 3y + 7z = 1 & \cdots③ \end{cases}$$

Eliminate ☐ :

Which is the easiest variable to eliminate?

⟨Ans.⟩

2 Solve each equation.

(1) $\begin{cases} 4x - 3y - 3z = -5 & \cdots ① \\ -x + 2y + z = 2 & \cdots ② \\ -3x + 5y + 2z = 7 & \cdots ③ \end{cases}$

Eliminate z:

② × 3 : $-3x + 6y + \boxed{}z = \boxed{}$ $\cdots ④$

① + ④ : $\cdots ⑤$

② × 2 : $\cdots ⑥$

③ − ⑥ :

⟨Ans.⟩ _____

(2) $\begin{cases} 3x - 2y - 7z = -7 & \cdots ① \\ 4x - 4y - 3z = 7 & \cdots ② \\ 5x + y - 8z = 8 & \cdots ③ \end{cases}$

Eliminate $\boxed{}$:

⟨Ans.⟩ _____

Do your best!

Simultaneous Linear Equations in Three Variables

Level

Score

Date   /   /

Name

100

1 **Solve each equation.**

50 points for completion

$$\begin{cases} 5x + 3y - 7z = -23 & \cdots① \\ 3x + 5y - 5z = -9 & \cdots② \\ 2x + 7y - 3z = 2 & \cdots③ \end{cases}$$

Eliminate x :

①× 3 : $\boxed{}x + 9y - 21z = -69$ $\cdots④$

②× $\boxed{}$: $15x + \boxed{}y - \boxed{}z = \boxed{}$ $\cdots⑤$

④ − ⑤ : $\boxed{}y + 4z = \boxed{}$ $\cdots⑥$

Simplify ⑥ :

$\boxed{}y + z = \boxed{}$ $\cdots⑦$

②× 2 :

③× 3 :

⟨**Ans.**⟩

2 **Solve each equation.**

50 points for completion

$$\begin{cases} -5x + 3y + 10z = 8 & \cdots ① \\ -7x + 5y + 8z = 2 & \cdots ② \\ -8x + 6y + 3z = -5 & \cdots ③ \end{cases}$$

⟨Ans.⟩

Your hard work really shows!

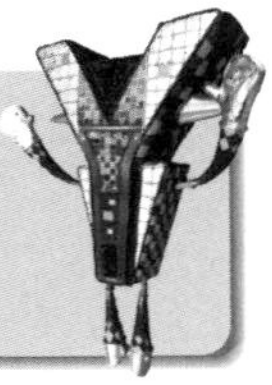

Word Problems with Simultaneous Linear Equations

12

Level

Score

/100

Date / /

Name

1   **Answer each word problem.**   25 points per question

(1)   Donald's class goes to a play, and the students must sit on benches. If 6 students sit on each bench, then 7 students will remain standing. If 8 students sit on each bench, then 1 student will remain standing. How many benches and how many students are there?

Let x be the number of benches and y be the number of students:

$$\begin{cases} 6x + 7 = y \\ \boxed{}x + 1 = y \end{cases}$$

⟨**Ans.**⟩   ☐ benches

☐ students

(2)   Irene's class takes a train back to school. If there are 3 students in each train car, then 16 must wait for the next train. If there are 5 students in each train car, then no students must wait. How many train cars and how many students are there?

⟨**Ans.**⟩

2　Answer each word problem.

25 points per question

(1)　Jeff's teacher has a bag of apples and oranges, where there are 3 times as many oranges as apples. If each student receives 2 apples, there is 1 apple left over. If each student receives 5 oranges, there are 7 oranges left over. How many students and apples are there?

Let x be the number of students and y be the number of apples:

$$\boxed{}\,x + 1 = y \ \cdots ①$$

Because y is the number of apples, and there are 3 times as many oranges as apples, there are $\boxed{}\,y$ oranges.

$$5x + 7 = \boxed{}\,y \ \cdots ②$$

Substitute ① into ② :

Substitute this into ① :

⟨**Ans.**⟩ _____

(2)　Ying's teacher has a box of pens and crayons, and there are 2 times as many crayons as pens. If each student receives 2 pens, there are 6 pens left over. If each student receives 5 crayons, there are 7 crayons left over. How many students and pens are there?

⟨**Ans.**⟩ _____

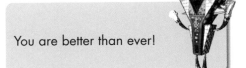

You are better than ever!

1 **Answer each word problem.**

25 points per question

（1） Warren rows 5 miles per hour. How many hours will it take him to row 20 miles?

Let x be the number of hours,

$5x = \boxed{}$

⟨**Ans.**⟩ _____

（2） Viola normally rows 10 miles per hour, but the wind is blowing against her at 2 miles per hour. How many hours will it take her to row 40 miles?

Viola normally rows 10 miles per hour,

but the wind is blowing against her at 2 miles per hour,

therefore Viola's speed is: $\left(10 - \boxed{}\right) = \boxed{}$ miles per hour.

Let x be the number of hours,

$\boxed{}\, x = 40$

⟨**Ans.**⟩ _____

（3） Rob normally rows 12 miles per hour, and the wind is pushing him along at 3 miles per hour. How many hours will it take him to row 45 miles?

⟨**Ans.**⟩ _____

2 Answer the word problem.

25 points for completion

Jane took 5 hours to row 40 miles against the current. She then turned around and took only 2 hours to row 60 miles with the current. How fast does Jane normally row (without any current), and how fast was the current?

Let x be Jane's normal speed and y be the speed of the current.

Because she took 5 hours to row 40 miles against the current:

$$(x - \boxed{}) \times 5 = 40$$

Because she took 2 hours to row 60 miles with the current:

$$(x + \boxed{}) \times 2 = 60$$

⟨**Ans.**⟩ Jane's speed:

The current's speed:

You show great dedication!

Inequalities

Date   /   /

Name

Level

Score

/100

---

1 **Solve each equation.**

2 points per question

> **Don't forget!**
>
> An **inequality** is a mathematical sentence that has a symbol such as $>$ or $<$. Solving an inequality is similar to solving an equation.
>
> **Examples**
>
> $x + 3 > 5$
>
> $x > 5 - 3$
>
> $x > 2$
>
> In the example to the left, the "$+3$" was transposed to the other side.
>
> $2x > 14$
>
> $x > 7$
>
> In the example to the left, both sides were divided by 2.
>
> The symbol $>$ is read as "is greater than," and the symbol $<$ is read as "is less than."

(1) $x + 2 > 8$

(2) $x + 5 > 2$

(3) $x - 6 > -2$

(4) $2x > 10$

(5) $3x > 12$

(6) $2x > 7$

---

2 **Solve each inequality.**

2 points per question

(1) $2x + 8 > 20$

$2x > 12$

$x > 6$

(2) $2x - 6 > 16$

(3) $3x + 9 > 12$

(4) $6x + 7 > 7$

3 **Solve each inequality.** 5 points per question

(1) $x - 3 < 7$

(2) $x - 4 < 9$

(3) $x + 8 < 6$

(4) $2x < 18$

(5) $5x < 13$

(6) $2x + 8 < 5$
$\quad\quad 2x < -3$

(7) $3x + 2 < -10$

(8) $4x - 8 < 6$

(9) $9x + 9 < 8$

4 **Solve each inequality.** 5 points per question

When multiplying or dividing an inequality by a negative number, reverse the inequality symbol.

Examples $\quad -2x < 6$ $\quad\quad\quad\quad\quad -3x > -15$
$\quad\quad\quad\quad\quad x > -3$ $\quad\quad\quad\quad\quad\quad\quad x < 5$

(1) $-2x < 10$
$\quad\quad x \boxed{} -5$

(2) $-x > -3$
$\quad\quad x \boxed{} 3$

(3) $-4x < 8$

(4) $-6x < -12$

(5) $-2x + 2 > -6$
$\quad\quad -2x > \boxed{}$

(6) $-6x - 8 > 4$

(7) $-x + 9 < -5$

You've got this!

Inequalities

15

Date   /   /

Name

---

1 **Solve each inequality.**

5 points per question

Inequalities with $\geq$ or $\leq$ are solved the same way as inequalities with $<$ or $>$.

Examples

$$x + 2 \geq 6$$
$$x \geq 4$$

$$-3x - 8 \leq 7$$
$$-3x \leq 15$$
$$x \geq -5$$

The symbol $\geq$ is read as "is greater than or equal to," and the symbol $\leq$ is read as "is less than or equal to."

(1) $2x + 5 \geq 7$

(5) $-2x - (x - 3) \geq -6$

(2) $-3x + 6 \leq 1$

(6) $-3x - (4 - 7x) \geq -10 + x$

(3) $5x - 2(x - 3) \leq 18$

$5x - \boxed{}x + \boxed{} \leq 18$

(7) $-3x - \left(\dfrac{1}{2} - x\right) \leq -2$

(4) $6x + 2(x + 4) \leq 8$

(8) $-5x - \left(\dfrac{3}{4}x - 1\right) \geq 3$

Don't forget to reverse the inequality symbol when multiplying or dividing an inequality by a negative number!

2 **Solve each inequality.**

Example $\dfrac{x-5}{3} > \dfrac{x-2}{4}$

Multiply both sides by the LCM of the denominators, 12:

$$4(x-5) > 3(x-2)$$
$$4x-20 > 3x-6$$
$$x > 14$$

(1) $\dfrac{x+4}{2} < \dfrac{x-7}{3}$

(4) $\dfrac{5x-1}{6} \geq \dfrac{3x+1}{4}$

(2) $\dfrac{2x-1}{5} \geq \dfrac{4x+5}{7}$

(5) $\dfrac{x+9}{3} \geq \dfrac{4x-5}{9}$

(3) $3x-5 \leq \dfrac{3-x}{4}$

(6) $\dfrac{3x-2}{4} < \dfrac{9x+8}{10}$

Think of solving an inequality like solving an equation.

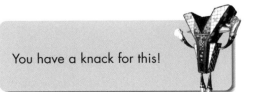

You have a knack for this!

31

Word Problems with Inequalities

Level ★

Date   /   /

Name

Score

/100

1 **Write each word problem as an inequality, and then solve.**

8 points per question

（1） x plus 6 is greater than four times x.

$$x + 6 > \boxed{}\, x$$

〈Ans.〉 _____

（2） y minus 8 is less than or equal to 6.

〈Ans.〉 _____

（3） 5 times z is greater than or equal to z plus 6.

〈Ans.〉 _____

（4） -2 multiplied by w is less than or equal to 3 less than w.

〈Ans.〉 _____

（5） The sum of 3 and q is greater than 8 times q.

〈Ans.〉 _____

2 **Write each word problem as an inequality, and then solve.** 15 points per question

(1) 3 times x plus 2 is less than 10.

$$\boxed{}\,x + 2 < \boxed{}$$

⟨**Ans.**⟩ _____

(2) 3 times the sum of x plus 2 is less than 10.

$$\boxed{}\,\left(x + \boxed{}\right) < 10$$

⟨**Ans.**⟩ _____

(3) 2 times the sum of $3x$ and 5 is greater than or equal to 9 times x.

⟨**Ans.**⟩ _____

(4) One half the difference of x and 4 is less than twice the difference of 5 and x.

$$\frac{1}{2}\left(x - \boxed{}\right) < 2\left(\boxed{} - x\right)$$

⟨**Ans.**⟩ _____

Hats off to you!

© Kumon Publishing Co., Ltd. 33

Inequalities
Range of x

Date / /   Name

---

1 **Draw each inequality on a number line.**　　　　　10 points per question

Example $x > 2$

The open dot (◯) shows that 2 is not included in the solution.

(1) $x < 4$

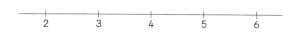

(3) $x > 0$

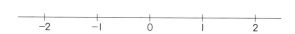

(2) $x > -1$

(4) $x > -\dfrac{1}{2}$

---

2 **Draw each inequality on a number line.**　　　　　10 points per question

Example $x \leq -1$

A closed dot (●) shows that -1 is included in the solution.

(1) $x \geq 0$

(2) $x \leq -\dfrac{5}{2}$

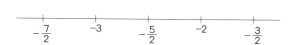

---

3 Draw each inequality on a number line to find the range of x that satisfies both inequalities.

10 points per question

Examples

$x > 1 \quad \cdots ①$
$x < 3 \quad \cdots ②$
⟨**Ans.**⟩ $1 < x < 3$

$x < 0 \quad \cdots ①$
$x > 1 \quad \cdots ②$
⟨**Ans.**⟩ No solution

The shaded region shows the range of x that satisfies both inequalities.

(1) $\begin{cases} x < 5 \quad \cdots ① \\ x > 2 \quad \cdots ② \end{cases}$

⟨**Ans.**⟩ $\boxed{} < x < \boxed{}$

(2) $\begin{cases} x > 6 \quad \cdots ① \\ x < 0 \quad \cdots ② \end{cases}$

⟨**Ans.**⟩ No solution

(3) $\begin{cases} x \geq -1 \quad \cdots ① \\ x < 0 \quad \cdots ② \end{cases}$

⟨**Ans.**⟩ $\boxed{} \leq x < \boxed{}$

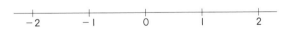

(4) $\begin{cases} x \leq -7 \quad \cdots ① \\ x \geq -10 \quad \cdots ② \end{cases}$

⟨**Ans.**⟩ $\boxed{} \leq x \leq \boxed{}$

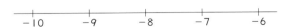

Nicely done!

Inequalities
Range of x

18

Level ★★

Date   /   /

Name

Score

/100

1 Draw each inequality on a number line to find the range of x that satisfies both inequalities.

4 points per question

Examples

$x > 1 \cdots$ ①
$x > 3 \cdots$ ②
⟨Ans.⟩ $x > 3$

$x > -2 \cdots$ ①
$x \geq 0 \cdots$ ②
⟨Ans.⟩ $x \geq 0$

(1) $\begin{cases} x < 3 & \cdots ① \\ x < -1 & \cdots ② \end{cases}$

⟨Ans.⟩

(2) $\begin{cases} x \geq 3 & \cdots ① \\ x > -3 & \cdots ② \end{cases}$

⟨Ans.⟩

(3) $\begin{cases} x \leq 4 & \cdots ① \\ x < 0 & \cdots ② \end{cases}$

⟨Ans.⟩

(4) $\begin{cases} x \geq 2 & \cdots ① \\ x \geq -1 & \cdots ② \end{cases}$

⟨Ans.⟩

(5) $\begin{cases} x \leq -4 & \cdots ① \\ x < -3 & \cdots ② \end{cases}$

⟨Ans.⟩

2 **Find the range of x that satisfies both inequalities.** 10 points per question

(1) $\begin{cases} x > 2 \\ x < 8 \end{cases}$

⟨Ans.⟩ _____

(2) $\begin{cases} x > 0 \\ x < -1 \end{cases}$

⟨Ans.⟩ _____

(3) $\begin{cases} x \geq 2 \\ x \geq -1 \end{cases}$

⟨Ans.⟩ _____

(4) $\begin{cases} x \leq -2 \\ x > -1 \end{cases}$

⟨Ans.⟩ _____

(5) $\begin{cases} x \leq 5 \\ x < -6 \end{cases}$

⟨Ans.⟩ _____

(6) $\begin{cases} 3x < 2x + 8 & \cdots① \\ 2x \geq 6 & \cdots② \end{cases}$

① becomes: $x < \boxed{}$

② becomes: $x \geq \boxed{}$

⟨Ans.⟩ $\boxed{} \leq x < \boxed{}$

(7) $\begin{cases} x > 4x - 6 & \cdots① \\ 5x - 3 > 7x + 9 & \cdots② \end{cases}$

① becomes:

② becomes:

⟨Ans.⟩ _____

(8) $\begin{cases} 6(x - 1) \leq -2(x + 3) & \cdots① \\ 2 - 6x < -2 + 2x & \cdots② \end{cases}$

① becomes:

② becomes:

⟨Ans.⟩ _____

You really know your stuff!

19 Word Problems with Inequalities

Level

Date / /

Name

Score
/ 100

1 Answer each word problem.

25 points per question

(1) Jack has 50 coins, and Tracey has 20 coins. They each give James the same amount of coins. Jack's new amount of coins is less than or equal to 4 times Tracey's new amount of coins. Find the range of the amount of coins they each could have given James.

Let x be the amount of coins they each gave James.

Jack's new amount of coins is: $50 - x$.

Tracey's new amount of coins is: $20 - \boxed{}$,

therefore $50 - x \leq \boxed{}\,(20 - \boxed{})$

⟨**Ans.**⟩ _____ coins or fewer

(2) Maria has 60 toys, and Alex has 40 toys. They each give Jane the same amount of toys. Alex's new amount of toys is greater than or equal to $\frac{1}{2}$ of Maria's new amount of toys. Find the range of the amount of toys they each could have given Jane.

⟨**Ans.**⟩ _____

2   Answer each word problem.

25 points per question

(1) Many boys and girls are playing in a park. There are twice as many girls as there are boys. If there are more than 60 children in the park, find the range of the amount of boys that could be in the park.

Let x be the number of boys.

Because there are twice as many girls as boys,

the number of girls is $\boxed{}\,x$.

Because there are more than 60 children,

$x + \boxed{}\,x > 60$

⟨**Ans.**⟩ _____ more than _____ boys

(2) Bruce sells TVs and radios at his store. The number of radios is half of the number of TVs. If there are at most 285 items in his store, find the range of the amount of radios.

⟨**Ans.**⟩ _____

This is tough. You're doing great!

1   Write the *x*-coordinate or *y*-coordinate of each point.

4 points per question

Examples

Point A: The *x*-coordinate is 1. The *y*-coordinate is 4.

Point B: The *x*-coordinate is − 1. The *y*-coordinate is 3.

- The *x*-**axis** is the horizontal number line, and the *y*-**axis** is the vertical number line.
- Each point is expressed as a pair of numbers called the *x*-**coordinate** and the *y*-**coordinate**.

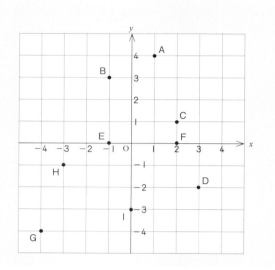

(1)   Point C: The *x*-coordinate is 2. The *y*-coordinate is ☐.

(2)   Point D: The *x*-coordinate is 3. The *y*-coordinate is ☐.

(3)   Point E: The *x*-coordinate is ☐. The *y*-coordinate is 0.

(4)   Point F: The *x*-coordinate is 2. The *y*-coordinate is ☐.

(5)   Point G: The *x*-coordinate is ☐. The *y*-coordinate is − 4.

(6)   Point H: The *x*-coordinate is ☐. The *y*-coordinate is ☐.

(7)   Point I : The *x*-coordinate is 0. The *y*-coordinate is ☐.

2 **Write the coordinates of each point.**

6 points per question

┌ Don't forget! ───────────────────────────────────

A point is expressed as a pair of coordinates or ordered pair. Write the x-coordinate and the y-coordinate inside the parentheses.

Example

The coordinates of point A are: $(3, -1)$

(1)   Point B: $\left(3,\ \boxed{}\right)$

(2)   Point C: $\left(\boxed{},\ -\dfrac{1}{2}\right)$

(3)   Point D: $\left(-\dfrac{3}{2},\ \boxed{}\right)$

(4)   Point E: $\left(\boxed{},\ \boxed{}\right)$

(5)   Point F: $\left(0,\ \boxed{}\right)$

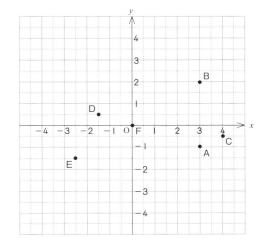

 Point F is located at the **origin**. The origin is where the x-axis and y-axis intersect.

3 **Answer each question.**

7 points per question

(1)   What are the coordinates of point A? $($, $)$

(2)   What are the coordinates of point B? $($, $)$

(3)   What are the coordinates of point C? $($, $)$

(4)   What are the coordinates of point D? $($, $)$

(5)   What are the coordinates of point E? $($, $)$

(6)   Which point is located at the origin? $\boxed{}$

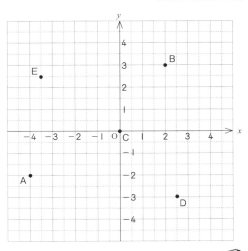

You are on point!

Graphs

21

Date   /   /

Name

Level

Score
/ 100

1 **Plot each point on the coordinate plane.**

5 points per question

Examples

Point A: $(-2, 0)$

Point B: $\left(\dfrac{1}{2}, 3\right)$

(1) Point C: $(2, 6)$

(2) Point D: $(0, 0)$

(3) Point E: $(2, -1)$

(4) Point F: $\left(-\dfrac{7}{2}, -6\right)$

(5) Point G: $(-3, 4)$

(6) Point H: $(-5, 0)$

(7) Point I: $(0, -4)$

(8) Point J: $\left(\dfrac{9}{2}, 2\right)$

(9) Point K: $\left(3, -\dfrac{5}{2}\right)$

(10) Point L: $\left(-\dfrac{7}{2}, -\dfrac{3}{2}\right)$

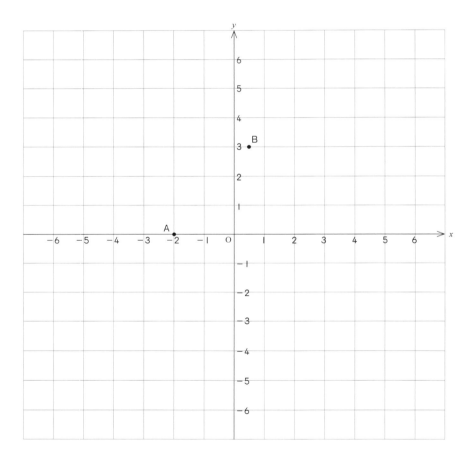

A point is expressed as a pair of coordinates in the form of: (x, y).

2 **Plot each point on the coordinate plane.**

(1) Point A: $(-3, 1)$

(2) Point B: $(0, -2)$

(3) Point C: $\left(-1, -\dfrac{3}{2}\right)$

(4) Point D: $\left(6, \dfrac{5}{2}\right)$

(5) Point E: $\left(-\dfrac{1}{2}, -\dfrac{9}{2}\right)$

(6) Point F: $\left(\dfrac{7}{2}, 4\right)$

(7) Point G: $(3, -6)$

(8) Point H: $(5, 0)$

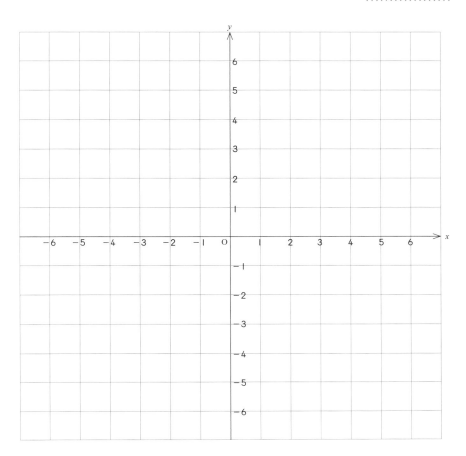

(9) Point ☐ lies on the x-axis

(10) Point ☐ lies on the y-axis

Well done!

22 Graphs

Date   /   /

Name

---

1 Find each value of y for the equation $y = 2x - 3$ according to each value of x.

4 points per question

(1) $x = -3$ $y = 2 \times (-3) - 3 =$

(2) $x = -2$ $y =$

(3) $x = -1$ $y =$

(4) $x = 0$ $y =$

(5) $x = 1$ $y =$

(6) $x = 2$ $y =$

(7) $x = 3$ $y =$

(8) $x = \dfrac{1}{2}$ $y =$

(9) $x = \dfrac{3}{4}$ $y =$

(10) $x = -\dfrac{3}{2}$ $y =$

2   **Graph the equation** $y = x - 2$ **by completing each exercise.**

(1)   Find each value of y according to each value of x.   5 points per question

①   A : $x = -2$ $y =$ ③   C : $x = 1$ $y =$

②   B : $x = 0$ $y =$ ④   D : $x = -\dfrac{1}{2}$ $y =$

(2)   Plot each of the above points on the coordinate plane, and then draw a line   20 points for completion
      to connect the points.

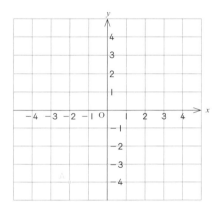

The line represents the graph of $y = x - 2$.

3   **Find each value of** y **for the equation** $y = -2x + 1$ **according to each**   20 points for completion
     value of x**. Then graph the equation.**

x	-1	$-\dfrac{1}{2}$	0	$\dfrac{1}{2}$	1	2
y						

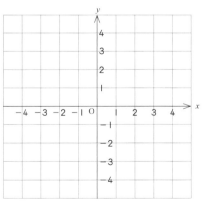

Nicely done!

Word Problems with Graphs

Level ★★

Score

/100

Date / /

Name

1 **Daniel walks at a speed of** 3 **miles per hour. Use this information to complete each exercise.**

10 points per question

(1) Let x represent the number of hours that Daniel walks, and let y represent the distance. Complete the chart to show the relationship between x and y.

x (hour)	0	1	2	2.5	3	4
y (mile)	0	3				

(2) Express the relationship between x and y as an equation.

$y = \boxed{} x$

(3) Graph the equation.

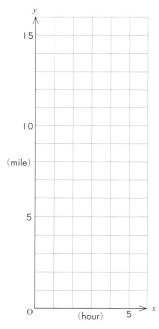

(4) How many miles has Daniel walked after 5 hours? Use the graph to answer.

⟨**Ans.**⟩ _____

Don't forget!

A **direct relation** is when the value of y increases as the value of x increases (and vice versa).

2 Jacob rows a boat at a speed of 12 miles per hour. Use this information to complete each exercise.

15 points per question

(1) Let x represent the number of hours that Jacob rows, and let y represent the distance. Complete the chart to show the relationship between x and y.

x (hour)	1	2	5	8	10
y (mile)					

(2) Express the relationship between x and y as an equation.

(3) Graph the equation.

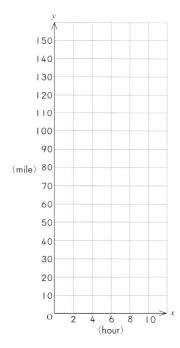

(4) How many miles has Jacob rowed after 7 hours? Use the equation to answer.

$y = 12 \times \boxed{} =$

⟨**Ans.**⟩

You're moving fast!

24 Word Problems with Graphs

Level ★★

Date / /

Name

Score

/ 100

1 Matt is practicing his jump shot. The chart below shows the relationship between the amount of time he practices (x minutes) and the number of baskets he makes (y baskets). Use the chart to complete each exercise.

12 points per question

x (minutes)	5	10	15	20
y (baskets)	10	20	30	40

(1) Express the relationship between x and y as an equation.

⟨Ans.⟩ _____

(2) Graph the equation.

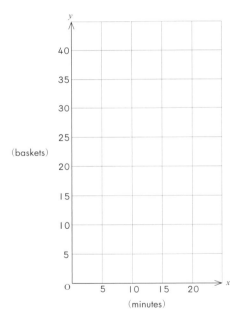

(3) How many baskets has Matt made after 18 minutes?

$y =$

⟨Ans.⟩ _____

2 Felix has a machine that makes gumballs. The chart below shows the relationship between the amount of time the machine works (x minutes) and the number of gumballs it makes (y gumballs). Use the chart to complete each exercise.

16 points per question

x (minutes)	2	3	5	8
y (gumballs)	16	24	40	64

(1) Express the relationship between x and y as an equation.

⟨**Ans.**⟩ _____

(2) Graph the equation.

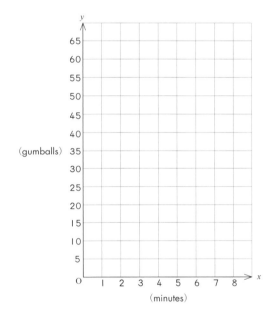

(gumballs)

(minutes)

(3) How many gumballs are made after 15 minutes? Use the equation to answer.

⟨**Ans.**⟩ _____

(4) How many gumballs are made after 9.5 minutes? Use the equation to answer.

⟨**Ans.**⟩ _____

Way to go!

Graphs
y-Intercept

25

Date / /

Name

Level ★★

Score /100

1 **Determine the y-intercept of each line.**

8 points per question

The **y-intercept** of a line is the y-coordinate of the point where the line crosses the y-axis.

Examples

The y-intercept of line (1) is −2.
The y-intercept of lines (2) and (3) is 3.

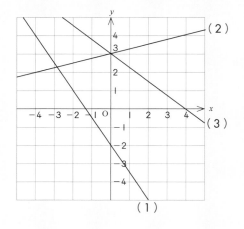

(1)   The y-intercept of line (1) is ☐.

(2)   The y-intercept of line (2) is ☐.

(3)   The y-intercept of line (3) is ☐.

(4)   The y-intercept of line (4) is ☐.

(5)   The y-intercept of line (5) is ☐.

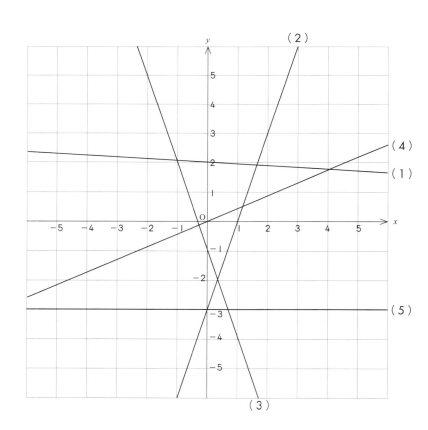

2   **Graph each equation to find the y-intercept.**

7 points per question

(1) The y-intercept of $y = 2x + 1$ is ☐.

(2) The y-intercept of $y = x - 3$ is ☐.

(3) The y-intercept of $y = \dfrac{3}{2}x - 1$ is ☐.

(4) The y-intercept of $y = \dfrac{1}{2}x + 4$ is ☐.

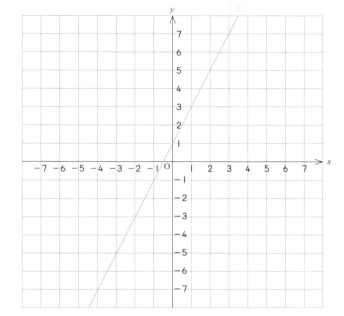

Label each line with the question number.

3   **Determine the y-intercept of each equation.**

8 points per question

Examples

The y-intercept of $y = 2x - 5$ is -5.
The y-intercept of $y = \dfrac{1}{2}x + 3$ is 3.

(1) The y-intercept of $y = 4x - 1$ is ☐.

(2) The y-intercept of $y = x + 2$ is ☐.

(3) The y-intercept of $y = \dfrac{1}{2}x - \dfrac{3}{5}$ is ☐.

(4) The y-intercept of $y = \dfrac{5}{3}x + \dfrac{16}{7}$ is ☐.

If you need to, make a table with the values of x and y.

You are doing really well!

  51

Graphs
Slope

Date   /   /   Name

Level ★★   Score   /100

1   **Determine the slope of each line.**

8 points per question

Don't forget!

The **slope** of a line describes the steepness of a line.

$$\text{slope} = \frac{rise}{run}$$

For example, the slope of line (1) is $\frac{3}{1}$ or 3 because the line rises 3 units vertically for every 1 unit it runs horizontally. The slope of line (2) is $\frac{1}{2}$ because the line rises 1 unit vertically for every 2 units it runs horizontally.

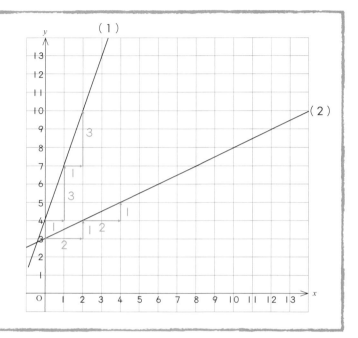

(1)   The slope of line (1) is ☐.

(2)   The slope of line (2) is ☐.

(3)   The slope of line (3) is ☐.

(4)   The slope of line (4) is ☐.

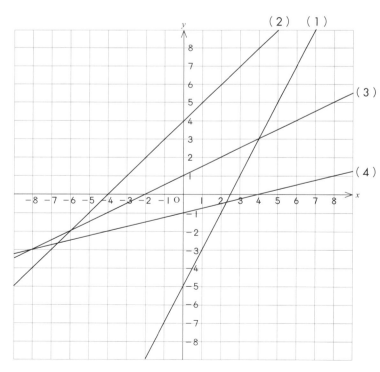

2   **Graph each equation to find the slope.**

7 points per question

(1)   The slope of $y = 3x$ is $\boxed{}$.

(2)   The slope of $y = x$ is $\boxed{}$.

(3)   The slope of $y = \dfrac{1}{2}x + 2$ is $\boxed{}$.

(4)   The slope of $y = \dfrac{2}{3}x - 3$ is $\boxed{}$.

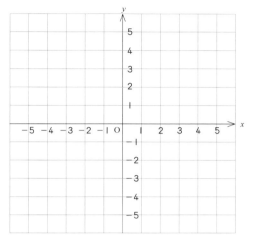

If you need to, make a table with the values of x and y.

3   **Determine the slope of each equation.**

8 points per question

Example

The slope of $y = 4x - 6$ is 4.

(1)   The slope of $y = 2x + 8$ is $\boxed{}$.

(4)   The slope of $y = \dfrac{5}{2}x$ is $\boxed{}$.

(2)   The slope of $y = 3x - \dfrac{1}{2}$ is $\boxed{}$.

(5)   The slope of $y = \dfrac{3}{8}x - \dfrac{7}{6}$ is $\boxed{}$.

(3)   The slope of $y = x + 6$ is $\boxed{}$.

Do your best!

27

Date　　/　　/

Name

---

1 **Graph each equation to find the slope.**

7 points per question

Examples

Lines (1) and (2) have a **negative slope**.

The slope of line (1) is -3 because the line falls 3 units vertically for every 1 unit it runs horizontally.

The slope of line (2) is $-\dfrac{1}{2}$ because the line falls 1 unit vertically for every 2 units it runs horizontally.

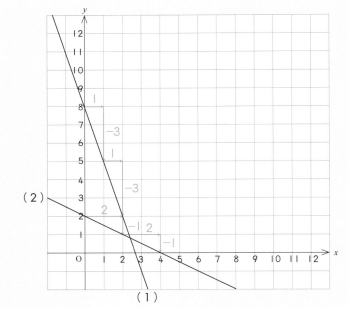

(1) The slope of $y = -2x + 2$ is ☐ .

x	0	1
y		

(2) The slope of $y = -x + 3$ is ☐ .

x	0	1
y		

(3) The slope of $y = -\dfrac{1}{2}x - 1$ is ☐ .

x	0	1	2
y			

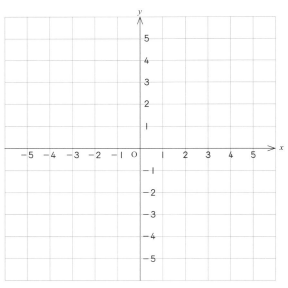

2 **Graph each equation to find the y-intercept.**　　　8 points per question

(1)　The y-intercept of $y=-3x$ is ☐ .

(2)　The y-intercept of $y=-x+\dfrac{1}{2}$ is ☐ .

(3)　The y-intercept of $y=\dfrac{1}{2}x-2$ is ☐ .

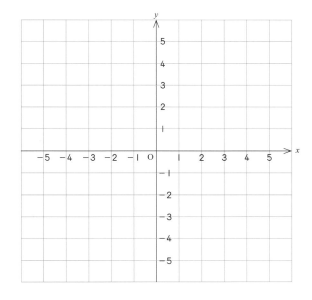

3 **Determine the slope and y-intercept of each equation.**　　11 points per question

(1)　$y=-3x+1$　　　　slope: ___−3___　　　y-intercept: _____

(2)　$y=-2x-6$　　　　slope: _____　　　y-intercept: _____

(3)　$y=-\dfrac{1}{2}x-2$　　　slope: _____　　　y-intercept: _____

(4)　$y=-\dfrac{5}{2}x$　　　　slope: _____　　　y-intercept: _____

(5)　$y=-6x-\dfrac{3}{5}$　　　slope: _____　　　y-intercept: _____

You understand slope and
y-intercept very well!

1 Graph each equation to find the slope and y-intercept.

10 points per question

(1) $y = 3x - 1$

slope: _____ y-intercept: _____

(2) $y = x + 2$

slope: _____ y-intercept: _____

(3) $y = -2x + 3$

slope: _____ y-intercept: _____

(4) $y = -x - 4$

slope: _____ y-intercept: _____

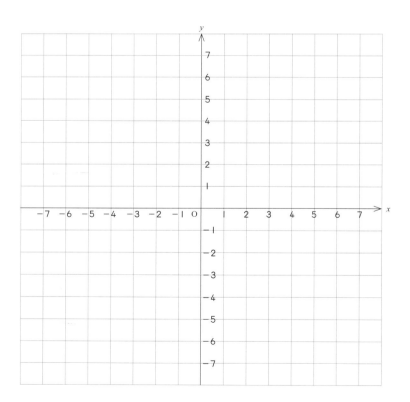

2 **Graph each equation to find the slope and y-intercept.**

15 points per question

(1)　$y = \dfrac{3}{2} x + 1$

slope: _____　y-intercept: _____

(2)　$y = \dfrac{1}{2} x - \dfrac{3}{2}$

slope: _____　y-intercept: _____

(3)　$y = -\dfrac{2}{3} x - 2$

slope: _____　y-intercept: _____

(4)　$y = -\dfrac{5}{2} x + \dfrac{1}{2}$

slope: _____　y-intercept: _____

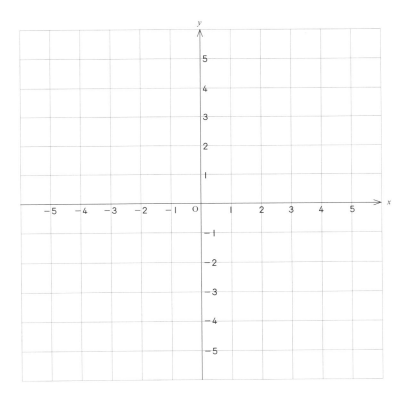

Practice makes perfect!

Date / /

Name

Score

/100

1 **Use the graph to complete each statement.**

5 points per question

(1) When the value of x is 0, the value of y is □.

(2) When the value of x is □, the value of y is 0.

(3) Therefore, when x changes from -3 to 0,

   y changes from 0 to □.

(4) Thus, as the value of x increases by 3,

   the value of y increases by □.

(5) In other words, as the value of x increases by 1,

   the value of y increases by □.

(6) The slope of the line is □.

(7) The y-intercept is □.

(8) The equation of the line is $y = $□$x + $□.

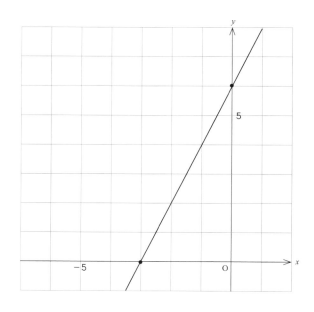

Don't forget!

If the relation between x and y can be expressed as $y = mx + b$, then the equation is called a **linear function**.

2 Use the graph to complete each statement.

5 points per question

(1) When the value of x is 0, the value of y is ☐.

(2) When the value of x is ☐, the value of y is 0.

(3) Therefore, when x changes from 0 to 6,

y changes from ☐ to 0.

(4) Thus, as the value of x increases by 6,

the value of y changes by ☐.

In other words, as the value of x increases

by 1, the value of y changes by ☐.

(5) The slope of the line is ☐, and the y-intercept is ☐.

(6) The equation of the line is $y =$ ☐$x +$ ☐.

3 Use the graph to complete each statement.

5 points per question

(1) When the value of x is 0, the value of y is ☐.

(2) When the value of x is ☐, the value of y is 0.

(3) Therefore, when x changes from -2 to 0,

y changes from 0 to ☐.

(4) Thus, as the value of x increases by 2,

the value of y changes by ☐.

In other words, as the value of x increases by 1,

the value of y changes by ☐.

(5) The slope of the line is ☐. The y-intercept is ☐.

(6) The equation of the line is: $y =$ ☐$x -$ ☐.

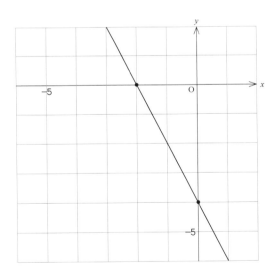

You're off to a great start with linear functions!

59

Linear Functions

Date   /   /

Name

Score

/100

1 Use the slope and y-intercept to graph each line.

10 points per question

(1) slope: 2, y-intercept: -3

(2) slope: 1, y-intercept: 0

(3) slope: -3, y-intercept: -1

(4) slope: $-\dfrac{3}{2}$, y-intercept: -3

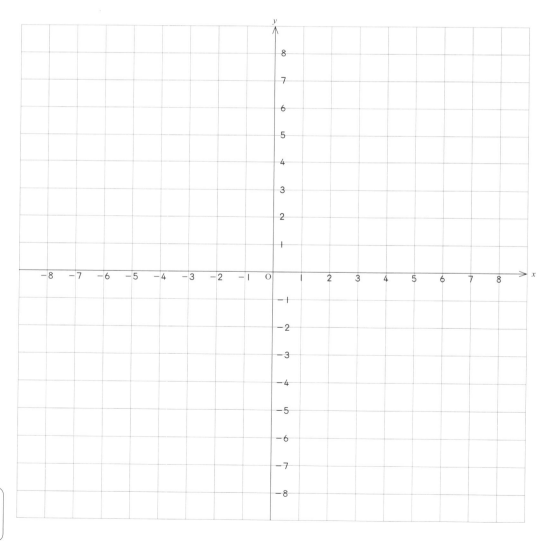

$$\text{slope} = \frac{\text{rise}}{\text{run}}$$

2   Use the slope and y-intercept to graph each line.

10 points per question

(1)   slope: 3, y-intercept: 3

(2)   slope: -4, y-intercept: 0

(3)   slope: $-\dfrac{5}{2}$, y-intercept: $-\dfrac{3}{2}$

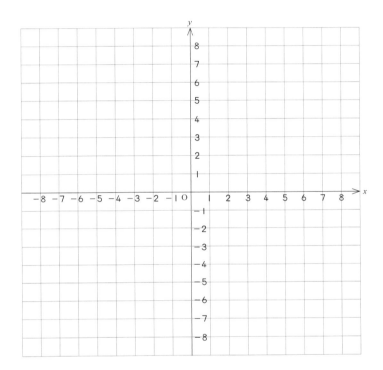

3   Determine the equation of each line above.

10 points per question

(1) $y = \boxed{}\, x + \boxed{}$

(2) $y = -$

(3) $y =$

You're doing so well!

Linear Functions

Date / /

Name

Level ★★

Score
/100

1 **Determine the equation of the line by completing each exercise.**

4 points per question

(1) The slope of the line is ☐.

(2) The y-intercept of the line is ☐.

(3) Therefore, the equation of the line is:

$$y = \boxed{}\, x - \boxed{}.$$

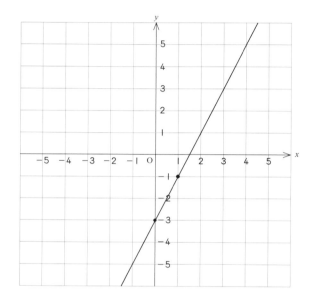

2 **Determine the equation of each line on the graph.**

8 points per question

(1) $y =$

(2) $y =$

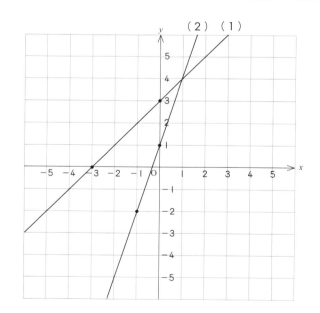

3 **Determine the equation of each line on the graph below.**

12 points per question

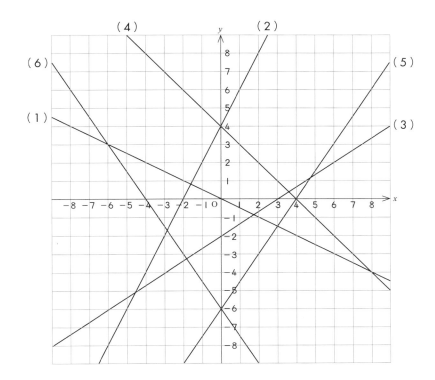

(1) $y =$

(2) $y =$

(3) $y =$

(4) $y =$

(5) $y =$

(6) $y =$

Good going!

Linear Functions

1 **Graph each line and determine the equation.**

25 points per question

(1) A line that passes through (1, 5) and has a slope of 2.

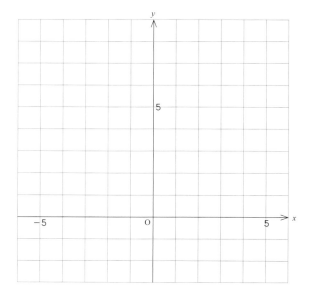

The y-intercept is ☐.

The equation of the line is: $y = 2x + $ ☐.

(2) A line that passes through $(-4, 3)$ and has a slope of $-\dfrac{1}{2}$.

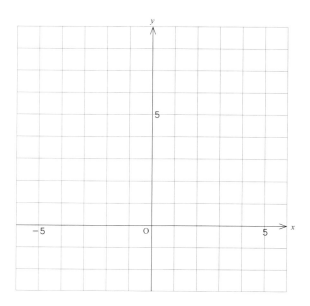

The y-intercept is ☐.

The equation of the line is:

2 **Determine the equation of each line and then graph it.** 25 points per question

(1) A line that passes through $(1, 4)$ and has a slope of -3.

Because the slope is -3,

$y = -3x + b \quad \cdots ①$

Because the line passes through $(1, 4)$,

substitute $(1, 4)$ into ①:

$4 = -3 \times \boxed{} + b$

$b = \boxed{}$

Substitute this into ①,

$y = -3x + \boxed{}$

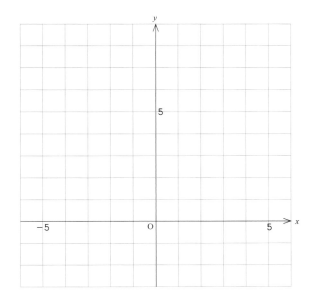

(2) A line that passes through $(-1, -2)$ and has a slope of $\dfrac{3}{2}$.

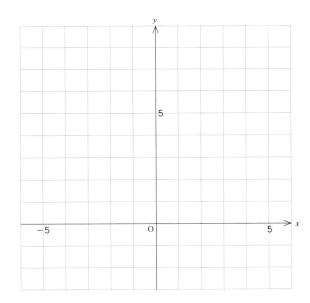

The letter b is used to represent an unknown value of the y-intercept.

Just superb!

Date / /

Name

1 **Find the slope of each line that passes through the given points.**

10 points per question

(1)

(1, 2) , (4, 7)

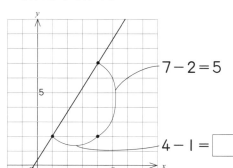

$7 - 2 = 5$

$4 - 1 = \boxed{}$

$$\text{slope} = \frac{5}{\boxed{}}$$

(3)

(2, 5) , (4, −3)

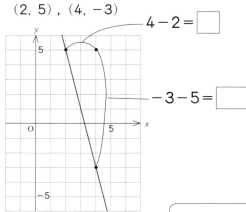

$4 - 2 = \boxed{}$

$-3 - 5 = \boxed{}$

$$\text{slope} = -\boxed{}$$

This line has a negative slope.

(2)

(−3, −2) , (1, 4)

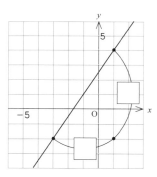

slope =

(4)

(−3, 2) , (1, −6)

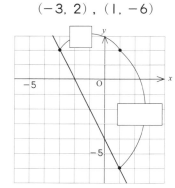

slope =

2 Find the slope of the line that passes through the given points.

10 points per question

Don't forget!

The slope of a line that passes through the points $(a,\ b)$ and $(c,\ d)$ is:

$$m = \frac{d-b}{c-a}$$

The letter m is used to represent slope.

Examples

$(1,\ 2)\ ,\ (4,\ 7)$

$$m = \frac{7-2}{4-1} = \frac{5}{3}$$

$(5,\ -1)\ ,\ (7,\ -3)$

$$m = \frac{-3-(-1)}{7-5} = -\frac{2}{2} = -1$$

(1) $(2,\ 8)\ ,\ (6,\ 9)$

$$m = \frac{9-8}{6-\boxed{}} = \frac{1}{\boxed{}}$$

(4) $(7,\ 0)\ ,\ (10,\ -2)$

$$m =$$

(2) $(0,\ -2)\ ,\ (4,\ 5)$

$$m =$$

(5) $(1,\ 1)\ ,\ (-1,\ 7)$

$$m =$$

(3) $(2,\ -6)\ ,\ (8,\ -3)$

$$m =$$

(6) $(-9,\ -5)\ ,\ (-3,\ -9)$

$$m =$$

Reduce the fraction if possible.

You're flying now!

Linear Functions

Date   /   /

Name

1   **A line passes through the points $(0, -1)$ and $(3, 5)$. Use this information to answer each exercise.**

    25 points per question

(1)   Determine the equation of the line.

Calculate the slope:

$$m = \frac{5 - (\boxed{})}{3 - \boxed{}} =$$

Let the equation of the line be:

$$y = \boxed{}\,x + b \cdots ①$$

Substitute $(0, -1)$ into ①:

$$\boxed{} = \boxed{} \times 0 + b$$

$$b = \boxed{}$$

Substitute this into ①:

$$y =$$

> You could also substitute $(3, 5)$ into ①.

(2)   Graph the equation.

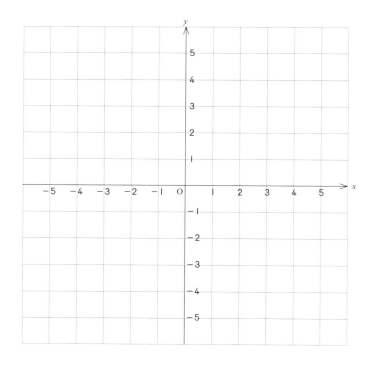

© Kumon Publishing Co., Ltd.

2 Find the equation of each line that passes through the given points, and then graph the equation.

25 points per question

(1) $(-1, 5)$, $(-2, -3)$

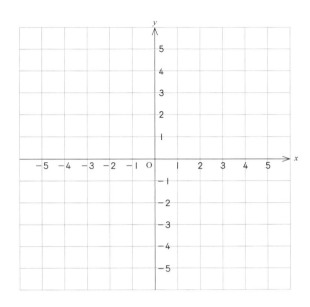

(2) $(-2, 3)$, $(4, -1)$

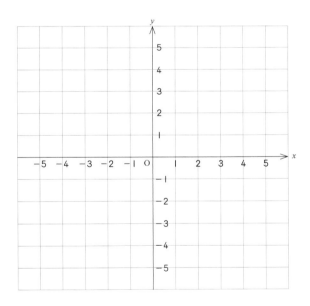

Carefully follow through on each step.

1 **Find the equation of each line.**

12 points per question

(1) A line that passes through $(2, 5)$ and has a slope of -1.

⟨**Ans.**⟩ _____

(2) A line that passes through $(-6, -1)$ and has a slope of $\dfrac{1}{2}$.

⟨**Ans.**⟩ _____

(3) A line that passes through the origin and has a slope of $-\dfrac{5}{3}$.

⟨**Ans.**⟩ _____

The origin is where the x-axis and y-axis meet, therefore the coordinates of the origin are: $(0, 0)$.

2 **Find the equation of each line.** 16 points per question

(1) A line that passes through $(1, 6)$ and $(3, 4)$.

⟨**Ans.**⟩ _____

(2) A line that passes through $(-4, -3)$ and $(2, 0)$.

⟨**Ans.**⟩ _____

(3) A line that passes through $(-1, 5)$ and the origin.

⟨**Ans.**⟩ _____

(4) A line that passes through $(1, 8)$ and has a y-intercept of 2.

Because the line has a y-intercept of 2, the line passes through $\left(\boxed{}, 2\right)$.

⟨**Ans.**⟩ _____

You've got this down, so let's move on to something new!

Date   /   /

Name

/100

---

1 **Graph each equation by finding the slope and y-intercept.**

20 points per question

(1) $2x + y = 5$

Transpose $2x$ to the right of the equal sign.

$y = \boxed{} + 5$

Therefore, the slope is $\boxed{}$,

and the y-intercept is $\boxed{}$.

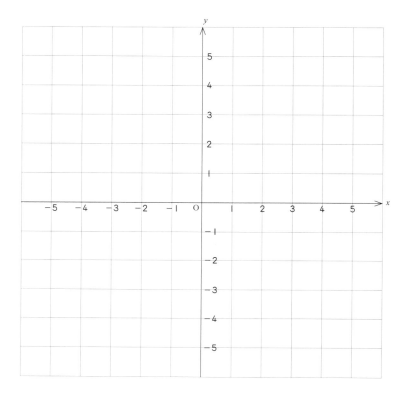

(2) $-3x + y = -4$

The slope is $\boxed{}$.

The y-intercept of the line is $\boxed{}$.

(3) $\dfrac{1}{2}x + y = -1$

The slope is $\boxed{}$.

The y-intercept of the line is $\boxed{}$.

Remember to label each line.

2 **Graph each equation by finding the slope and y-intercept.**

20 points per question

(1) $2x + 3y = 12$

Transpose $2x$ to the right of the equal sign.

$$3y = \boxed{} + 12$$

$$y = \boxed{} + 4$$

Therefore, the slope is $\boxed{}$,

and the y-intercept is $\boxed{}$.

(2) $-6x - 2y = 1$

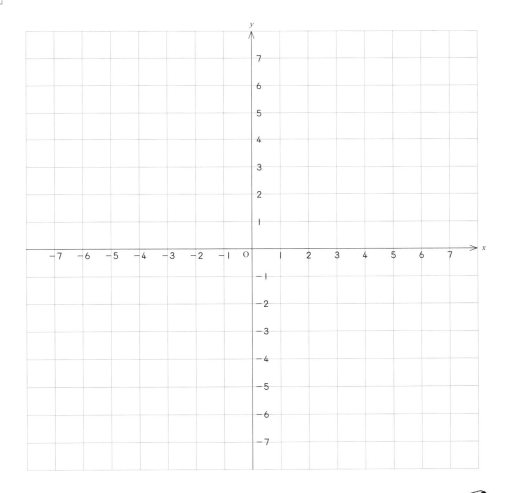

You are doing stellar work!

Simultaneous Linear Equations

Level ★★★

Score

/100

1 **Use the simultaneous linear equations** $\begin{cases} 3x+y=-1 & \cdots① \\ -x+y=3 & \cdots② \end{cases}$ **for each exercise.**

25 points per question

(1) Find the point of intersection by graphing.

Rewrite ①: $y = \boxed{} - 1 \quad \cdots③$

Rewrite ②: $y = \quad \cdots④$

Graph ③ and ④:

Point of intersection: $(x, y) = (,)$

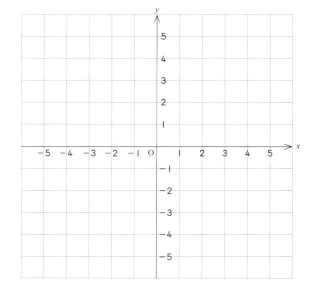

Don't forget!

The **point of intersection** is a point where two or more lines cross.

---

(2) Find the point of intersection by solving the simultaneous linear equations algebraically.

$\begin{cases} 3x+y=-1 & \cdots① \\ -x+y=3 & \cdots② \end{cases}$

Point of intersection: $(x, y) = (,)$

You can find the point of intersection by graphing both equations or solving them algebraically.

2 Use the simultaneous linear equations $\begin{cases} x - 2y = 7 & \cdots ① \\ -3x + y = -6 & \cdots ② \end{cases}$ for each exercise.

25 points per question

(1) Find the point of intersection by graphing.

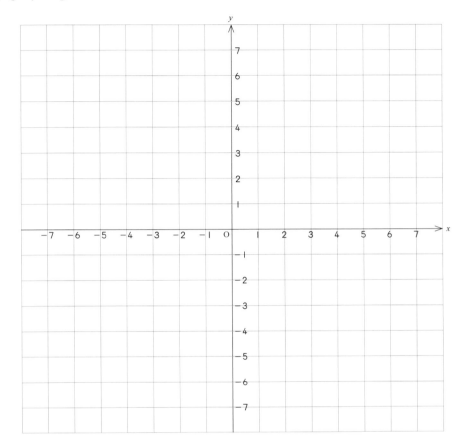

Point of intersection: $(x, y) = ($, $)$

(2) Find the point of intersection by solving the simultaneous linear equations algebraically.

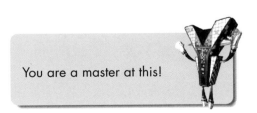

You are a master at this!

Point of intersection: $(x, y) = ($, $)$

38

Horizontal and Vertical Lines

Level ★★★

Date   /   /

Name

Score

/ 100

Don't forget!

The equation for a **horizontal line** is $y = a$ (where a represents a number). Horizontal lines have a slope of 0.

Example

$y = 3$

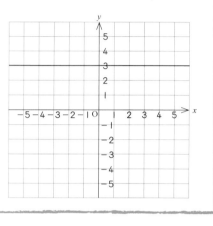

1 **Graph each equation.**

10 points per question

(1) $y = -3$

(2) $y - 4 = 0$

Rewrite the equation: $y = \boxed{}$

(3) $2y - 3 = 0$

(4) $2y + 1 = 0$

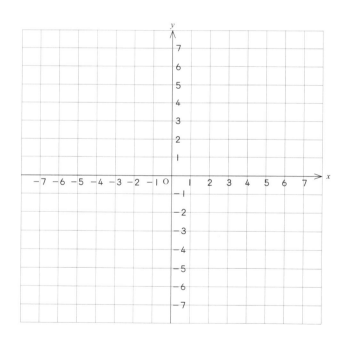

Don't forget!

The equation for a **vertical line** is $x = a$ (where a represents a number). The slope of a vertical line does not exist.

Example

$x = -2$

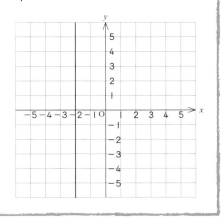

---

2 **Graph each equation.**

10 points per question

(1) $x = 4$

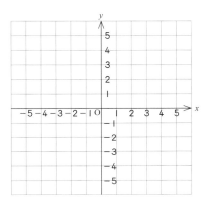

(2) $x + 5 = 0$

(3) $3x + 6 = 0$

---

3 **Graph each equation.**

10 points per question

(1) $2x + y = 3$

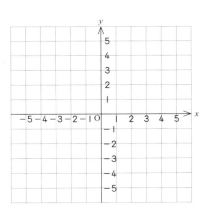

(2) $2x = 3$

(3) $y = 3$

Keep up the good work!

77

Parallel Lines

1 **Graph the lines** $\begin{cases} y = 2x + 4 & \cdots ① \\ y = 2x - \dfrac{1}{2} & \cdots ② \end{cases}$ **and answer the question.**

25 points for completion

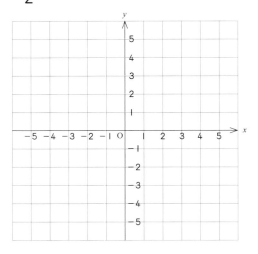

How many points of intersection do the two lines have? The two lines have ☐ points of intersection.

┌─ Don't forget! ───

Parallel lines are lines that have the same slope but different y-intercepts. Parallel lines do not have any points of intersection.

2 **Graph** $\begin{cases} 6x + 3y = 12 & \cdots ① \\ -4x - 2y = 1 & \cdots ② \end{cases}$ **to show that they are parallel lines.**

25 points for completion

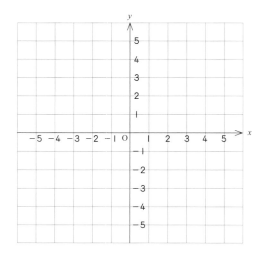

3 Find the equation of the line that is parallel to the given line and passes through the given point.

25 points per question

(1) $y = 2x + 3$; $(-1, -6)$

Because the line is parallel to $y = 2x + 3$,

the slope of the line is also $\boxed{}$.

Because the slope is $\boxed{}$,

$y = \boxed{}x + b$.

Because the line passes through $(-1, -6)$,

⟨**Ans.**⟩ _____

(2) $x + 4y = -6$; $(8, -3)$

⟨**Ans.**⟩ _____

You can figure out any line!

Perpendicular Lines

Score

/100

Date / /

Name

1 **Graph each equation.**

10 points per question

(1) $y = \frac{2}{3}x + 1$

(2) $y = -\frac{3}{2}x - 2$

(3) $y = -\frac{3}{2}x + 7$

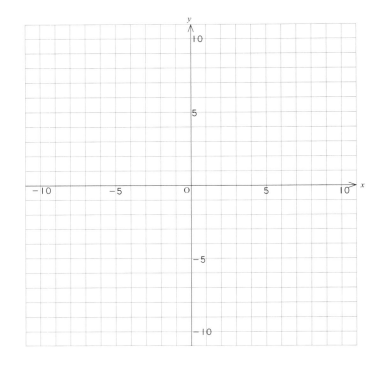

 The slope of line (1) has the opposite sign and is the reciprocal of the slope of line (2); therefore line (1) is perpendicular to line (2).

2 **Given that line ① is perpendicular to line ②, complete each exercise.**

10 points per question

(1) If the slope of line ① is $\frac{3}{4}$, then the slope of line ② is $\boxed{-\frac{4}{3}}$.

(2) If the slope of line ① is $-\frac{7}{2}$, then the slope of line ② is $\boxed{}$.

(3) If the slope of line ① is 6, then the slope of line ② is $\boxed{}$.

3 **Find the equation of the line that is perpendicular to each given line and passes through each given point.** 20 points per question

(1) $y = \dfrac{2}{3}x + 5$; $(-4, -1)$

Because the line is perpendicular to $y = \dfrac{2}{3}x + 5$, the slope of the line is $\boxed{}$.

Because the slope is $\boxed{}$, $y = \boxed{}x + b$.

Because the line passes through $(-4, -1)$,

⟨Ans.⟩ _____

(2) $4x + 8y = 3$; $(-6, -7)$

Rewrite the equation:

$8y = -4x + 3$

$y =$

⟨Ans.⟩ _____

I'm impressed!

81

Perpendicular Lines

Level ★★★

Score

Date / /

Name

/100

1 Find the equation of the line that is perpendicular to the given line and passes through the given point.

25 points per question

(1) $3x - 2y = 5$; $(-3, -1)$

⟨Ans.⟩ _____

(2) $-5x = \dfrac{1}{2}y - 1$; $\left(\dfrac{1}{4}, \dfrac{1}{2}\right)$

⟨Ans.⟩ _____

2 The equation for Line A is $-6x+4y=-8$. **Use this information to find the equation for each line, and then graph each line below.**

25 points per question

(1) Line B is parallel to Line A and passes through $(-3, 1)$.

⟨**Ans.**⟩ _____

(2) Line C is perpendicular to Line A and passes through $(-3, 1)$.

⟨**Ans.**⟩ _____

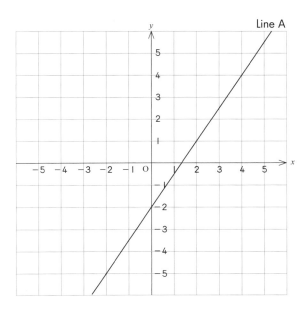

Fantastic work!

Review

42

Date / /

Name

Level ⭐⭐

Score

/100

1 Use the following method to solve the equations $\begin{cases} 6x + 5y = 8 & \cdots ① \\ -4x + 3y = 20 & \cdots ② \end{cases}$. 10 points per question

(1) Addition/subtraction method

(2) Substitution method

⟨Ans.⟩ _____

⟨Ans.⟩ _____

2 Answer the word problem. 14 points for completion

Nori's farm has several rabbits and chicks. There are 3 times as many chicks as rabbits. If each member of Nori's family holds 2 rabbits, there are 3 rabbits left over. If each family member holds 3 chicks, there are 27 chicks left over. How many people make up Nori's family? How many chicks are there?

⟨Ans.⟩ _____ people in Nori's family

_____ chicks

3 Solve each inequality.

10 points per question

(1) $2(x+5) - \dfrac{1}{2}x < 2$

(3) $-\dfrac{9-x}{2} < \dfrac{-3-x}{4}$

(2) $-3x - 2\left(\dfrac{1}{4}x - \dfrac{1}{2}\right) \geq 2 - x$

(4) $\dfrac{3x+2}{5} \geq \dfrac{-x+4}{2}$

4 Solve each inequality or find the range of x that satisfies both inequalities.

13 points per question

(1) $\begin{cases} 3x > -x + 8 \\ 5 - x > x + 9 \end{cases}$

(2) $\begin{cases} 4\left(3 - \dfrac{1}{2}x\right) \geq 3(1 + 2x) \\ -\left(-\dfrac{1}{2}x - 1\right) \leq 2(1 - 3x) \end{cases}$

〈Ans.〉

〈Ans.〉

You're almost at the finish line!

1 **Graph each equation.**

15 points per question

(1) $3x + y = 2$

(3) $3x + 5y = 0$

(2) $4x - y = 0$

(4) $-2x + 6y = 3$

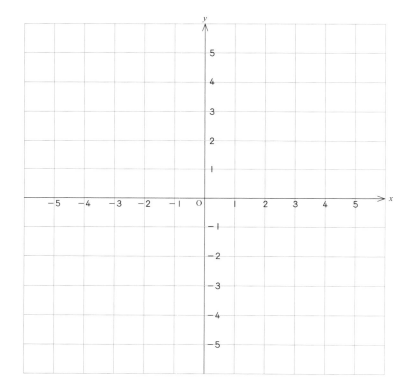

2 **Use each method to find the point of intersection of**

20 points per question

$$\begin{cases} 2x - 4y = -14 & \cdots ① \\ 12x + 8y = 12 & \cdots ② \end{cases}.$$

(1) Graph the equations to find the point of intersection.

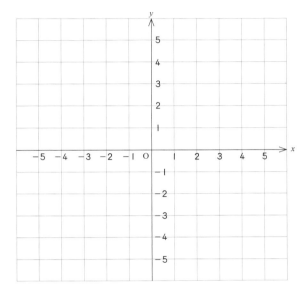

Point of intersection: $(x, y) = ($, $)$

(2) Use algebra to find the point of intersection.

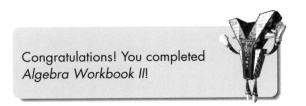

Congratulations! You completed
Algebra Workbook II!

Point of intersection: $(x, y) = ($, $)$

(1) Solving Equations Review pp 2, 3

(1)
(1) $x = 11$ (6) $x = -\dfrac{3}{4}$
(2) $x = 6$ (7) $x = \dfrac{7}{3}$
(3) $x = 1$ (8) $x = \dfrac{1}{12}$
(4) $x = -8$ (9) $x = -\dfrac{11}{3}$
(5) $x = -4$ (10) $x = \dfrac{11}{6}$

(2)
(1) $x = 5$ (6) $x = \dfrac{15}{2}$
(2) $x = -24$ (7) $x = -\dfrac{9}{2}$
(3) $x = -\dfrac{4}{3}$ (8) $x = -\dfrac{1}{15}$
(4) $x = -1$ (9) $x = \dfrac{2}{3}$
(5) $x = 10$ (10) $x = \dfrac{1}{2}$

(2) Solving Equations Review pp 4, 5

(1)
(1) $x = 3$ (5) $x = \dfrac{3}{2}$
(2) $x = 2$ (6) $x = -\dfrac{14}{5}$
(3) $x = -4$ (7) $x = -\dfrac{7}{2}$
(4) $x = -5$ (8) $x = -\dfrac{15}{4}$

(2)
(1) $x = 7$
  Left side $= 3 \times 7 - 6 = 15$
  Right side $= 7 + 8 = 15$
(2) $x = 3$
  Left side $= 2 \times 3 + 15 = 21$
  Right side $= 9 \times 3 - 6 = 21$
(3) $x = 1$
  Left side $= -\dfrac{1}{3} \times 1 + \dfrac{1}{2} = \dfrac{1}{6}$
  Right side $= \dfrac{5}{3} \times 1 - \dfrac{3}{2} = \dfrac{1}{6}$
(4) $x = 4$
  Left side $= -\dfrac{1}{2} \times 4 - \dfrac{1}{3} = -\dfrac{7}{3}$
  Right side $= -\dfrac{3}{4} \times 4 + \dfrac{2}{3} = -\dfrac{7}{3}$

(3) Solving Equations Review pp 6, 7

(1)
(1) $x = -5$ (4) $x = -\dfrac{2}{3}$
(2) $x = 2$ (5) $x = -\dfrac{21}{2}$
(3) $x = \dfrac{9}{5}$

(2)
(1) $x = y - 3$ (6) $x = -\dfrac{b}{4}$
(2) $x = -b - c$ (7) $x = \dfrac{b}{a}$
(3) $x = -w + y$ (8) $x = \dfrac{4a + b}{9}$
(4) $x = -f + 3$ (9) $x = \dfrac{-2b + 3c}{a}$
(5) $x = -w - 8$ (10) $x = \dfrac{s + 4t}{r}$

(4) Simultaneous Linear Equations Review pp 8, 9

(1)
(1) Ans. $(x, y) = (-1, 2)$ (3) Ans. $(x, y) = \left(\dfrac{1}{2}, -4\right)$
(2) Ans. $(x, y) = (-4, -3)$ (4) Ans. $(x, y) = \left(-3, -\dfrac{2}{3}\right)$

(2)
(1) Ans. $(x, y) = (-1, -2)$ (3) Ans. $(x, y) = \left(4, -\dfrac{2}{3}\right)$
(2) Ans. $(x, y) = \left(-\dfrac{3}{5}, 3\right)$ (4) Ans. $(x, y) = (-6, -2)$

(5) Simultaneous Linear Equations Review pp 10, 11

(1)
(1) Ans. $(x, y) = (2, -3)$ (2) Ans. $(x, y) = (2, 1)$

(2)
(1) Ans. $(x, y) = (-4, 2)$
  ① : $\boxed{-4} - 2 \times \boxed{2} = -8$
  ② : $2 \times \boxed{(-4)} + 3 \times \boxed{2} = -2$
(2) Ans. $(x, y) = \left(-\dfrac{1}{2}, \dfrac{2}{3}\right)$

(6) Simultaneous Linear Equations Review pp 12, 13

(1)
(1) Ans. $(x, y) = (2, -2)$ (2) $\boxed{4}$ Ans. $(x, y) = (3, -1)$

(2)
(1) Ans. $(x, y) = (4, 2)$
(2) Ans. $(x, y) = (4, 3)$
(3) Ans. $(x, y) = (5, -4)$

7 Simultaneous Linear Equations Review pp 14, 15

1 (1) Ans. $(x, y)=(-2, -5)$ (3) Ans. $(x, y)=(4, -3)$

(2) Ans. $(x, y)=(-7, -2)$ (4) Ans. $(x, y)=(1, 1)$

2 (1) $\boxed{-2}$ (3) $\boxed{-4x-1}$

Ans. $(x, y)=(-3, 4)$ Ans. $(x, y)=(2, -3)$

(2) Ans. $(x, y)=(5, 1)$ (4) Ans. $(x, y)=(3, 1)$

8 Simultaneous Linear Equations Review pp 16, 17

1 (1) Ans. $(x, y)=(1, -3)$ (2) Ans. $(x, y)=(1, -3)$

2 (1) Ans. $(x, y)=(-2, -5)$ (2) Ans. $(x, y)=(-2, -5)$

3 (1) Ans. $(x, y)=(-5, -3)$ (2) Ans. $(x, y)=(-5, -3)$

4 (1) Ans. $(x, y)=(4, -6)$ (2) Ans. $(x, y)=(4, -6)$

9 Simultaneous Linear Equations in Three Variables pp 18, 19

1 (1) $\boxed{5}$, $\boxed{2}$, $\boxed{-2}$, $\boxed{3}$, $\boxed{3}$, $\boxed{5}$, $\boxed{-4}$, $\boxed{2}$, $\boxed{3}$, $\boxed{2}$, $\boxed{3}$, $\boxed{2}$, $\boxed{1}$ Ans. $(x, y, z)=(\boxed{1}, \boxed{3}, \boxed{2})$

(2) Ans. $(x, y, z)=(-3, -2, 2)$

2 (1) $\boxed{11}$, $\boxed{9}$, $\boxed{-5}$ Ans. $(x, y, z)=(4, -2, 1)$

(2) Ans. $(x, y, z)=(1, -4, 1)$

10 Simultaneous Linear Equations in Three Variables pp 20, 21

1 (1) Ans. $(x, y, z)=(3, 1, 2)$

(2) $\boxed{y}$ Ans. $(x, y, z)=(-5, -1, 4)$

2 (1) $\boxed{3}$, $\boxed{6}$ Ans. $(x, y, z)=(-2, 1, -2)$

(2) $\boxed{y}$ Ans. $(x, y, z)=(6, 2, 3)$

11 Simultaneous Linear Equations in Three Variables pp 22, 23

1 $\boxed{15}$, $\boxed{5}$, $\boxed{25}$, $\boxed{25}$, $\boxed{-45}$, $\boxed{-16}$, $\boxed{-24}$, $\boxed{-4}$,

$\boxed{-6}$ Ans. $(x, y, z)=(-3, 2, 2)$

---

2 Ans. $(x, y, z)=(-2, -4, 1)$

12 Word Problems with Simultaneous Linear Equations pp 24, 25

1 (1) $\begin{cases} 6x+7=y \\ \boxed{8}x+1=y \end{cases}$

Ans. $\boxed{3}$ benches
$\boxed{25}$ students

(2) Let x be the number of train cars and y be the number of students:

$\begin{cases} 3x+16=y \\ 5x=y \end{cases}$

Ans. 8 train cars
40 students

2 (1) $\boxed{2}$, $\boxed{3}$, $\boxed{3}$

Ans. 4 students
9 apples

(2) Let x be the number of students and y be the number of pens:

$\begin{cases} 2x+6=y \\ 5x+7=2y \end{cases}$

Ans. 5 students
16 pens

13 Word Problems with Simultaneous Linear Equations pp 26, 27

1 (1) $5x=\boxed{20}$ Ans. 4 hours

(2) $\boxed{2}$, $\boxed{8}$, $\boxed{8}x=40$ Ans. 5 hours

(3) $15x=45$ Ans. 3 hours

2 $(x-\boxed{y})\times 5=40$

$(x+\boxed{y})\times 2=60$

Ans. Jane's speed: 19 miles per hour
The current's speed: 11 miles per hour

14 Inequalities pp 28, 29

1 (1) $x>6$ (4) $x>5$

(2) $x>-3$ (5) $x>4$

(3) $x>4$ (6) $x>\dfrac{7}{2}$

2 (1) $2x>12$ (3) $x>1$

$x>6$

(2) $x>11$ (4) $x>0$

3 (1) $x < 10$ (6) $2x < -3$

(2) $x < 13$ $x < -\dfrac{3}{2}$

(3) $x < -2$ (7) $x < -4$

(4) $x < 9$ (8) $x < \dfrac{7}{2}$

(5) $x < \dfrac{13}{5}$ (9) $x < -\dfrac{1}{9}$

4 (1) $x \boxed{\geq} -5$ (5) $\boxed{-8}$, $x < 4$

(2) $x \boxed{\leq} 3$ (6) $x < -2$

(3) $x > -2$ (7) $x > 14$

(4) $x > 2$

---

15 **Inequalities** pp 30, 31

1 (1) $x \geq 1$ (5) $x \leq 3$

(2) $x \geq \dfrac{5}{3}$ (6) $x \geq -2$

(3) $\boxed{2}$, $\boxed{6}$, $x \leq 4$ (7) $x \geq \dfrac{3}{4}$

(4) $x \leq 0$ (8) $x \leq -\dfrac{8}{23}$

2 (1) $x < -26$ (4) $x \geq 5$

(2) $x \leq -\dfrac{16}{3}$ (5) $x \leq 32$

(3) $x \leq \dfrac{23}{13}$ (6) $x > -\dfrac{26}{3}$

---

16 **Word Problems with Inequalities** pp 32, 33

1 (1) $x + 6 > \boxed{4}x$ **Ans.** $x < 2$

(2) $y - 8 \leq 6$ **Ans.** $y \leq 14$

(3) $5z \geq z + 6$ **Ans.** $z \geq \dfrac{3}{2}$

(4) $-2w \leq w - 3$ **Ans.** $w \geq 1$

(5) $3 + q > 8q$ **Ans.** $q < \dfrac{3}{7}$

2 (1) $\boxed{3}x + 2 < \boxed{10}$ **Ans.** $x < \dfrac{8}{3}$

(2) $\boxed{3}(x + \boxed{2}) < 10$ **Ans.** $x < \dfrac{4}{3}$

(3) $2(3x + 5) \geq 9x$ **Ans.** $x \leq \dfrac{10}{3}$

(4) $\dfrac{1}{2}(x - \boxed{4}) < 2(\boxed{5} - x)$ **Ans.** $x < \dfrac{24}{5}$

---

17 **Inequalities** Range of x pp 34, 35

1 (1) (3)

(2) (4)

2 (1) (2)

3 (1) **Ans.** $\boxed{2} < x < \boxed{5}$

(2) **Ans.** No solution

(3) **Ans.** $\boxed{-1} \leq x < \boxed{0}$

(4) **Ans.** $\boxed{-10} \leq x \leq \boxed{-7}$

---

18 **Inequalities** Range of x pp 36, 37

1 (1) **Ans.** $x < -1$

(2) **Ans.** $x \geq 3$

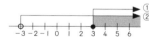

(3) **Ans.** $x < 0$

(4) **Ans.** $x \geq 2$

(5) **Ans.** $x \leq -4$

2 (1) **Ans.** $2 < x < 8$ (5) **Ans.** $x < -6$

(2) **Ans.** No solution (6) $\boxed{8}$, $\boxed{3}$, **Ans.** $\boxed{3} \leq x < \boxed{8}$

(3) **Ans.** $x \geq 2$ (7) **Ans.** $x < -6$

(4) **Ans.** No solution (8) **Ans.** No solution

(19) Word Problems with Inequalities pp 38, 39

1 (1) $\boxed{x}$, $50 - x \le \boxed{4}(20 - \boxed{x})$

$\quad\quad\quad x \le 10$ **Ans.** 10 coins or fewer

(2) Let x be the number of toys Maria and Alex each

gave Jane.

$40 - x \ge \dfrac{1}{2}(60 - x)$

$\quad x \le 20$ **Ans.** 20 toys or fewer

2 (1) $\boxed{2}$, $x + \boxed{2}x > 60$ **Ans.** more than 20 boys

(2) Let x be the amount of radios.

$x + 2x \le 285$

$\quad x \le 95$

    Ans. less than or equal to 95 radios

(20) Graphs pp 40, 41

1 (1) $\boxed{1}$

(2) $\boxed{-2}$

(3) $\boxed{-1}$

(4) $\boxed{0}$

(5) $\boxed{-4}$

(6) $\boxed{-3}$, $\boxed{-1}$

(7) $\boxed{-3}$

2 (1) $\boxed{2}$

(2) $\boxed{4}$

(3) $\boxed{\dfrac{1}{2}}$

(4) $\boxed{-\dfrac{5}{2}}$, $\boxed{-\dfrac{3}{2}}$

(5) $\boxed{0}$

3 (1) $(-4, -2)$

(2) $(2, 3)$

(3) $(0, 0)$

(4) $\left(\dfrac{5}{2}, -3\right)$

(5) $\left(-\dfrac{7}{2}, \dfrac{5}{2}\right)$

(6) $\boxed{C}$

(21) Graphs pp 42, 43

1
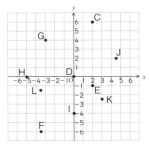

2
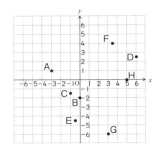

(9) $\boxed{H}$

(10) $\boxed{B}$

(22) Graphs pp 44, 45

1 (1) $2 \times (-3) - 3 = -9$ (6) 1

(2) -7 (7) 3

(3) -5 (8) -2

(4) -3 (9) $-\dfrac{3}{2}$

(5) -1 (10) -6

2 (1) ① -4

② -2

③ -1

④ $-\dfrac{5}{2}$

(2)
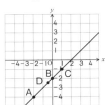

3

x	-1	$-\dfrac{1}{2}$	0	$\dfrac{1}{2}$	1	2
y	3	2	1	0	-1	-3

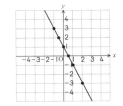

23 Word Problems with Graphs pp 46, 47

1 (1)

x (hour)	0	1	2	2.5	3	4
y (mile)	0	3	6	7.5	9	12

(2) $y = \boxed{3}x$

(3)
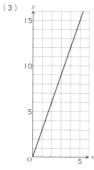

(4) **Ans.** 15 miles

2 (1)

x (hour)	1	2	5	8	10
y (mile)	12	24	60	96	120

(2) $y = 12x$

(3)
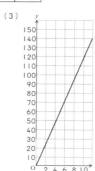

(4) $y = 12 \times \boxed{7} = 84$

Ans. 84 miles

24 Word Problems with Graphs pp 48, 49

1 (1) **Ans.** $y = 2x$

(2)

(3) $y = 2 \times 18 = 36$

Ans. 36 baskets

2 (1) **Ans.** $y = 8x$

(2)
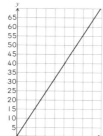

(3) $y = 8 \times 15 = 120$

Ans. 120 gumballs

(4) $y = 8 \times 9.5 = 76$

Ans. 76 gumballs

25 Graphs y-Intercept pp 50, 51

1 (1) $\boxed{2}$

(2) $\boxed{-3}$

(3) $\boxed{-1}$

(4) $\boxed{0}$

(5) $\boxed{-3}$

2 (1) $\boxed{1}$

(2) $\boxed{-3}$

(3) $\boxed{-1}$

(4) $\boxed{4}$

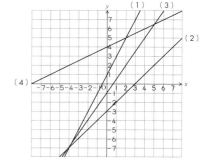

3 (1) $\boxed{-1}$

(2) $\boxed{2}$

(3) $\boxed{-\dfrac{3}{5}}$

(4) $\boxed{\dfrac{16}{7}}$

26 Graphs Slope pp 52, 53

1 (1) $\boxed{2}$

(2) $\boxed{1}$

(3) $\boxed{\dfrac{1}{2}}$

(4) $\boxed{\dfrac{1}{4}}$

2 (1) $\boxed{3}$

(2) $\boxed{1}$

(3) $\boxed{\dfrac{1}{2}}$

(4) $\boxed{\dfrac{2}{3}}$

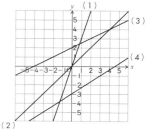

3 (1) $\boxed{2}$

(2) $\boxed{3}$

(3) $\boxed{1}$

(4) $\boxed{\dfrac{5}{2}}$

(5) $\boxed{\dfrac{3}{8}}$

27 **Graphs** Slope   pp 54,55

1 (1) $\boxed{-2}$

x	0	1
y	2	0

(2) $\boxed{-1}$

x	0	1
y	3	2

(3) $\boxed{-\dfrac{1}{2}}$

x	0	1	2
y	-1	$-\dfrac{3}{2}$	-2

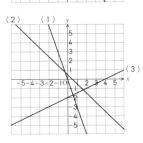

2 (1) $\boxed{0}$

(2) $\boxed{\dfrac{1}{2}}$

(3) $\boxed{-2}$

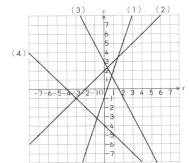

3 (1) -3, 1

(2) -2, -6

(3) $-\dfrac{1}{2}$, -2

(4) $-\dfrac{5}{2}$, 0

(5) -6, $-\dfrac{3}{5}$

28 **Graphs**   pp 56,57

1 (1) 3, -1

(2) 1, 2

(3) -2, 3

(4) -1, -4

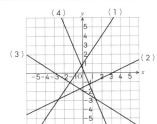

2 (1) $\dfrac{3}{2}$, 1

(2) $\dfrac{1}{2}$, $-\dfrac{3}{2}$

(3) $-\dfrac{2}{3}$, -2

(4) $-\dfrac{5}{2}$, $\dfrac{1}{2}$

29 **Linear Functions**   pp 58,59

1 (1) $\boxed{6}$

(2) $\boxed{-3}$

(3) $\boxed{6}$

(4) $\boxed{6}$

(5) $\boxed{2}$

(6) $\boxed{2}$

(7) $\boxed{6}$

(8) $y = \boxed{2}x + \boxed{6}$

2 (1) $\boxed{2}$

(2) $\boxed{6}$

(3) $\boxed{2}$

(4) $\boxed{-2}$, $\boxed{-\dfrac{1}{3}}$

(5) $\boxed{-\dfrac{1}{3}}$, $\boxed{2}$

(6) $y = \boxed{-\dfrac{1}{3}}x + \boxed{2}$

3 (1) $\boxed{-4}$

(2) $\boxed{-2}$

(3) $\boxed{-4}$

(4) $\boxed{-4}$, $\boxed{-2}$

(5) $\boxed{-2}$, $\boxed{-4}$

(6) $y = \boxed{-2}x - \boxed{4}$

30 **Linear Functions**   pp 60,61

1

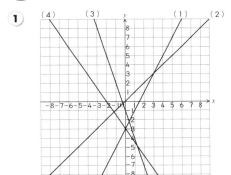

2

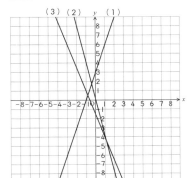

3 (1) $y = \boxed{3}x + \boxed{3}$

(2) $y = -4x$

(3) $y = -\dfrac{5}{2}x - \dfrac{3}{2}$

93

31 Linear Functions
pp 62, 63

1 (1) $\boxed{2}$

(2) $\boxed{-3}$

(3) $y = \boxed{2}x - \boxed{3}$

2 (1) $y = x + 3$

(2) $y = 3x + 1$

3 (1) $y = -\dfrac{1}{2}x$

(2) $y = 2x + 4$

(3) $y = \dfrac{2}{3}x - 2$

(4) $y = -x + 4$

(5) $y = \dfrac{3}{2}x - 6$

(6) $y = -\dfrac{3}{2}x - 6$

32 Linear Functions
pp 64, 65

1 (1) $\boxed{3}$, $y = 2x + \boxed{3}$

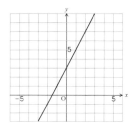

(2) $\boxed{1}$, $y = -\dfrac{1}{2}x + 1$

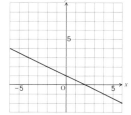

2 (1) $\boxed{1}$, $\boxed{7}$, $y = -3x + \boxed{7}$

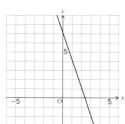

(2) $y = \dfrac{3}{2}x - \dfrac{1}{2}$

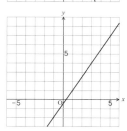

33 Linear Functions
pp 66, 67

1 (1) $\boxed{3}$,

slope $= \dfrac{5}{\boxed{3}}$

(2) $1 - (-3) = \boxed{4}$,

$4 - (-2) = \boxed{6}$,

slope $= \dfrac{3}{2}$

(3) $4 - 2 = \boxed{2}$, $-3 - 5 = \boxed{-8}$,

slope $= -\boxed{4}$

(4) $1 - (-3) = \boxed{4}$,

$-6 - 2 = \boxed{-8}$,

slope $= -2$

2 (1) $\dfrac{9 - 8}{6 - \boxed{2}} = \dfrac{1}{\boxed{4}}$

(2) $\dfrac{7}{4}$

(3) $\dfrac{1}{2}$

(4) $-\dfrac{2}{3}$

(5) -3

(6) $-\dfrac{2}{3}$

34 Linear Functions
pp 68, 69

1 (1) $m = \dfrac{5 - (\boxed{-1})}{3 - \boxed{0}} = 2$

$y = \boxed{2}x + b$

$\boxed{-1} = \boxed{2} \times 0 + b$

$b = \boxed{-1}$

$y = 2x - 1$

(2)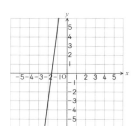

2 (1) $y = 8x + 13$

(2) $y = -\dfrac{2}{3}x + \dfrac{5}{3}$

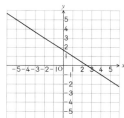

35 Linear Functions
pp 70, 71

1 (1) **Ans.** $y = -x + 7$

(2) **Ans.** $y = \dfrac{1}{2}x + 2$

(3) **Ans.** $y = -\dfrac{5}{3}x$

2 (1) **Ans.** $y = -x + 7$

(2) **Ans.** $y = \dfrac{1}{2}x - 1$

(3) **Ans.** $y = -5x$

(4) **Ans.** $\boxed{0}$, $y = 6x + 2$

36 Linear Functions

pp72,73

1 (1) $y = \boxed{-2x} + 5$

$\boxed{-2}$

$\boxed{5}$

(2) $\boxed{3}$, $\boxed{-4}$

(3) $\boxed{-\dfrac{1}{2}}$, $\boxed{-1}$

2 (1) $3y = \boxed{-2x} + 12$

$y = \boxed{-\dfrac{2}{3}}x + 4$

$\boxed{-\dfrac{2}{3}}$

$\boxed{4}$

(2) $y = -3x - \dfrac{1}{2}$

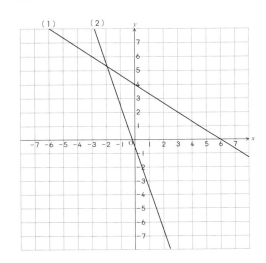

37 Simultaneous Linear Equations

pp74,75

1 (1) $y = \boxed{-3x} - 1$

$y = x + 3$

$(x, y) = (-1, 2)$

(2) $\begin{cases} y = -3x - 1 \\ y = x + 3 \end{cases}$

$(x, y) = (-1, 2)$

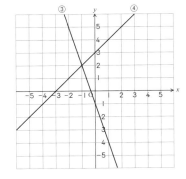

2 (1) $(1, -3)$

(2) $(1, -3)$

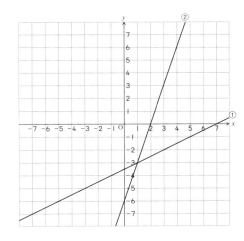

38 Horizontal and Vertical Lines

pp76,77

1 (1) $y = -3$

(2) $y = \boxed{4}$

(3) $y = \dfrac{3}{2}$

(4) $y = -\dfrac{1}{2}$

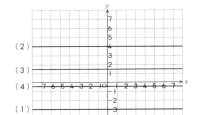

2

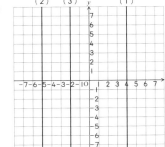

3

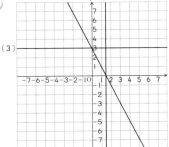

(39) Parallel Lines

pp 78, 79

1

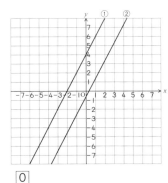

0

2

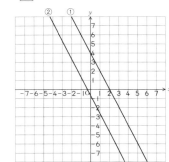

3 (1) [2], [2], $y = $[2]$x + b$ **Ans.** $y = 2x - 4$

(2)   **Ans.** $y = -\dfrac{1}{4}x - 1$

(40) Perpendicular Lines

pp 80, 81

1

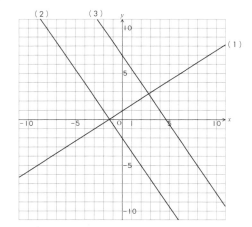

2 (1) $\boxed{-\dfrac{4}{3}}$

(2) $\boxed{\dfrac{2}{7}}$

(3) $\boxed{-\dfrac{1}{6}}$

3 (1) $\boxed{-\dfrac{3}{2}}$, $\boxed{-\dfrac{3}{2}}$, $y = \boxed{-\dfrac{3}{2}}x + b$ **Ans.** $y = -\dfrac{3}{2}x - 7$

(2)   **Ans.** $y = 2x + 5$

(41) Perpendicular Lines

pp 82, 83

1 (1) **Ans.** $y = -\dfrac{2}{3}x - 3$

(2) **Ans.** $y = \dfrac{1}{10}x + \dfrac{19}{40}$

2 (1) **Ans.** $y = \dfrac{3}{2}x + \dfrac{11}{2}$

(2) **Ans.** $y = -\dfrac{2}{3}x - 1$

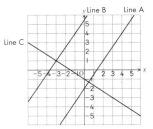

(42) Review

pp 84, 85

1 (1) **Ans.** $(x, y) = (-2, 4)$,   **Ans.** $(x, y) = (-2, 4)$

2   Let x be the number of people in Nori's family,
and y be the number of rabbits. There are $3y$ chicks.

$$\begin{cases} 2x + 3 = y \\ 3x + 27 = 3y \end{cases}$$

Ans. 6 people in Nori's family
45 chicks

3 (1) $x < -\dfrac{16}{3}$ (3) $x < 5$

(2) $x \leq -\dfrac{2}{5}$ (4) $x \geq \dfrac{16}{11}$

4 (1) **Ans.** No solution   (2) **Ans.** $x \leq \dfrac{2}{13}$

(43) Review

pp 86, 87

1

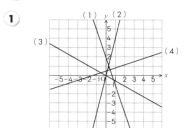

2 (1) **Ans.** $(-1, 3)$

(2) **Ans.** $(-1, 3)$

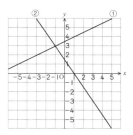